THOUGHT

AND

WISDOM

THOUGHT

AND

WISDOM

C. West Churchman

INTERSYSTEMS PUBLICATIONS

of the SYSTEMS INQUIRY SERIES

To
Russ Ackoff
for the years of friendship

TABLE OF CONTENTS

PREFACE

The title of this book may seem pretentious but it is not intended to be. "Thought" and "Wisdom" are depicted here as two conversationalists. It is not my intention to spell out in full the meaning of wisdom but it is my intention to express my love of it.

Nor is the conversation in any respect a true debate. The two conversationalists agree on many things and the many things are generally the products of thought.

If you like, Thought is an aging system approacher rather set in his ways. Wisdom is a lot younger and probably feminine. Both Thought and Wisdom agree that the three cornerstones of philosophy, the Good, the True, and the Beautiful, are closely intertwined; but Thought does emphasize the True, and Wisdom the Good and the Beautiful. In effect, Wisdom's ethics are based on the aesthetic.

You can imagine that, following the definition of conversation in the book, the conversation exists in a place, perhaps a cabin overlooking the vast expanse of the Pacific Ocean.

Finally, the conversation is about Thought's love of Wisdom, and might therefore have been called Thought's philosophy.

Bolinas, California
Armistice Day, 1981

i

FOREWORD

Part I of this book consists of the H. Rowan Gaither Lectures, delivered May 1981, at the University of California, Berkeley, under the sponsorship of the Graduate School of Business Administration and the Center for Research in Management.

These lectures in systems science are named in memory of one of the founders and the first Chairman of the Board of the RAND Corporation. They were established by gift of the System Development Corporation, formerly a division of the RAND Corporation.

Part II consists of papers written in recent years that closely relate to the subject matter of the Gaither Lectures.

PART I

PART I

1

ON CONNECTEDNESS:
PUTTING THE WORLD TOGETHER

I still remember the astonishment I felt when, about two years ago, I was called to jury duty in Marin County, California. A group of us formed a panel, and a random selection process asked one person after another to answer some questions. One of the questions (apparently of central importance) asked the prospective juror whether he or she could separate in his mind the process of judging whether a certain young man was guilty or innocent of an armed robbery of a restaurant, from the processes that would follow (e.g., imprisonment or release).

To me the answer was perfectly obvious: of course not. Here was a system one of the components of which was a jury trial, and another component was the so-called criminal justice system which I had long since decided was fraught with inequities. The jury trial had a reasonable chance of throwing the young man into the jaws of this criminal justice system. How could I conceivably stand up and declare that the two processes — the trial and the subsequent justice system — were systemically separable?

But to my astonishment, one after another of my fellow citizens unhesitatingly answered the judge in the affirmative. Indeed, none of them even asked his honor to explain what the question meant (to a systems philosopher its meaning is quite obscure). Not all the candidate jurors were selected. (One loving wife of a police officer actually believed that officers make more accurate witnesses than non-officers — a devotion beyond the call of marital duty, I'd say.) But none was rejected because he declared he could not separate the trial from its possible aftermaths.

So I sat there with considerable nervousness as to what I should say when called upon. This set in motion a conversation within me. My uppity ego said I should tell the judge "I am a systems expert and the question is absurd since the answer is obviously 'no'. All social systems are strongly nonseparable with respect to their components, and this one is clearly no exception. If your honor would take the time to read a few of my books, you'd know this is so and not bother us by asking foolish questions." My more cautious (cowardly?) side asked whether such a reply might not evoke a "contempt of court" sentence. "But I *am* contemptuous of the court," said the brave ego. Luckily the random number system wisely never got to call me.

When I got home I thought I could see why everyone else was so quick to say "yes." To them, it must have seemed obvious that the young man had entered the restaurant at a certain time and used a gun to demand money, or else he had not done anything of the kind. The past contained one of these two facts, and the jury trial was being used to determine which fact had occurred. It was not being used to draw inferences about what should happen in the future to the young man; that would be up to the judge, parole officers, prison officers, etc.

But to me this piece of ontology was quite deceptive. One could believe, reasonably enough, that history contains an episode at a certain place and time (the happenings in the restaurant at 6:16 p.m. on a certain date), but decide *not* to undergo the process of discovering whether history contains it. To use perhaps too superficial an example, I do believe that beneath the surface of my front yard there are some old gold pieces, or else not. But nothing would induce me to take shovel in hand to try to find out, even if I had found a letter in the house from some prior resident saying he had buried them there, because my front yard contains plants which I dearly love.

The point is that once you dig for facts or coins, you change a lot of other things as well, and these changes may not be ones you want. Of course, I think most of the potential jurors would recognize one feature of the situation that makes fact-finding nonseparable from the aftermath, namely, that they may determine the fact incorrectly, a common enough mistake on the part of juries no matter how sincere and "objective" they try to be. But I suppose that most of them believe the error could be as much one way as the other: to incarcerate the innocent is (for them) about the same as freeing the guilty. Indeed, they are not alone in this regard: science's typical way of expressing its finding in terms of a sample mean plus or minus an error term expresses the same idea. In the case of science, one often doesn't know the "other things" that people will create from the findings, but surely a guilty man free in the streets is a totally different event from an innocent man in a cell. Since I'm fairly sure that the system that holds people in cells — innocent or not — is incredibly inequitable, how can I willfully join a subsystem — the jury trial — that so often puts people there?

I really should not have been too surprised at the behavior of my fellow jurors, because I've been living a lifetime among fellow academics who firmly believe there is a clear distinction between the determination of facts and the determination of ethical values. I suspect they have no adequate defense of the argument just given which connects the two determinations ("should this particular fact be determined?" is an ethical issue); but I also suspect they have never posed the issue in this manner. What has been strange to me is that operations researchers, city planners, policy analysts, and others of their kind, also believe that the separation of fact-determination from ethical-determination is real. Indeed, many of them do not seem to believe that the determination of ethical values belongs to their business, which is essentially an inquiry into plans.

To illustrate, this is the ninth and last of the Gaither Lectures in Systems Science, the first having been given by Charles Hitch[1] in 1965. With one exception, none of the lecturers addressed the question of the proper determination of ethical values at all, even though I believe that every one of them assumed some ethical foundation in his work. Hitch assumed that there should be a well-designed military administration in

---

1.   Charles J. Hitch, *Decision-making for Defense* (Berkeley, CA: University of California Press, 1965).

this country. Schultze[2] assumed that there are good and bad (evil?) budget designs. Rivlin[3] assumed that social experimentation should be conducted for the good of the country. Macy[4] implicitly assumed that public broadcasting, if "properly" conducted, is a "good thing," well worth fighting for. Vickers[5] believed that our social world is in peril, and society needs redesigning of responsibilities to reduce the peril. Simon[6] said that the use of artificial intelligence to bring some of us up to the level of being "satisficed" is a good thing. Raiffa,[7] whose topic surely called for an ethical discussion since he dealt with arbitration and negotiation, cleverly shied away from all ethical issues except those dealing with his version of logical consistency. The exception was Jantsch[8] who did discuss at some length the relationship between matters of morality and his theory of universal evolution. But he lets method (paradigm) lead, and ethics come second.

The story of the Gaither Lectures is repeated in many other contexts: city planning departments which practically forbid classroom discussion of ethics, operations research texts which never mention ethical issues the student may confront in the future, public policy schools which ignore the ethical foundations of policy, and so on. Schools of business administration in the USA often have departments which teach courses on law and society where ethical issues are addressed, but ethics are handled by case methods or exercises rather than reading the history of ethics. Furthermore, ethics is treated as a separate subject, and rarely, if ever,

---

2.   Charles L. Schultze, *The Politics and Economics of Public Spending* (Washington, D.C.: The Brookings Institution, 1968).

3.   Alice M. Rivlin, *Systematic Thinking for Social Action* (Washington, D.C.: The Brookings Institution, 1971).

4.   John W. Macy, Jr., *To Irrigate a Wasteland* (A Quantum Book, Berkeley, CA: University of California Press, 1974).

5.   Sir Geoffrey Vickers, *Responsibility — Its Sources and Limits* (The Systems Inquiry Series, Seaside, CA: Intersystems Publications, 1980).

6.   Herbert A. Simon, *The Sciences of the Artificial Revisited* (Cambridge, MA: MIT Press, 1969, 2nd ed. 1981).

7.   Howard Raiffa, *The Art & Science of Negotiation* (Cambridge, MA: Harvard University Press, 1982).

8.   Erich Jantsch, *The Self-organizing Universe* (The Systems Science and World Order Library, Elmsford, NY: Pergamon Press, 1980).

integrated into other course topics, e.g., marketing, accounting, finance, etc.

If I may add one more mystery to the story of today's separation of ethics and sciences: the avoidance of the issue of how to determine ethically justified values is a fairly recent occurrence in the so-called "scientific" community. In the classical age of Greek science, from the pre-Socratics through Plato, Aristotle, and on into the Hellenistic period, the issue was central to all science. Much more recently, the age that saw the creation of modern science, and most especially the seventeenth and eighteenth centuries in the West, regarded ethical issues as among the most important ones that science must face. I leave it to those who are more astute than I in understanding historical causes, to tell us what happened in the nineteenth century that turned the intellectual community away from basic ethical issues. I sometimes suspect that my most beloved and admired Kant had a lot to do with it. Rather, it was Kant's idea that the creation of knowledge of the phenomenal world[9] is totally different from the creation of moral knowledge, that did the trick. The post-Kantian scientists then concluded that intellectually one could dwell in the first world and simply have "non-scientific" opinions in the second, a conclusion that I am sure Kant never intended.

The title of this book is "Thought and Wisdom." I've adapted a design idea from Tchaikovsky's Fifth Symphony, namely, that the conversation between thought and wisdom will appear in all the chapters, but not in the same version. Here, I would like to suggest one notion of the topic, namely, that wisdom is thought combined with a concern for ethics. This is a highly intellectual idea about wisdom, and may indeed emanate from thought itself. In any event, it leads me to say that the science of Leibniz, Spinoza, Hume, and Kant of the seventeenth and eighteenth centuries was far wiser than the so-called science of the twentieth century.

Now it is both right and natural for the curious mind to ask what "ethics" is and to supplement this question with two others, whether ethics can be taught and if so who are the experts to teach it? My own

---

9.   Immanuel Kant, *Critique of Pure Reason*, 1781.

answers to these queries do not comply with the manner in which ethics is taught in most business schools, namely, as a conversation between a professor and his students on cases in business where ethical issues seem to be critical. Rather, because I believe ethics to be a universal topic, applicable in all times and places, I take "ethics" to be a conversation with our ancestors and contemporaries on the meaning of right and wrong conduct, policies, management, planning, etc., or, what is the same, on good and evil in all these domains of human decision making. I do not believe there are any experts on ethical issues per se, but, of course, there can be excellent guides in creating good conversations with our ancestors by helping students to read them intelligently. The group of ancestors I'd put together would include the very oldest: the *I Ching,* the *Bhagavad Gita,* the pre-Socratics, Plato, Artistotle, Epicurus, the Stoics, St. Paul, St. Augustine, St. Thomas, Spinoza, Hume, some holy books, and whoever one wants to select from more recent history. The conversation is not only the attempt to understand what an ancestor says, but what his sayings mean in the design of our lives.

This book is, in effect, an example of one such conversation. I can continue the conversation by mentioning one epistemology that seems to pervade a lot of today's planning.

To give this epistemology a label, I'll call it bounded systems thinking. It begins with the ontological assumption that the world of human affairs consists of problems and possible solutions: problems really exist, and the first task is to identify and describe them, a task that is not radically different from an entomologist's description of insects in a given volume of earth.

These planners differ from the natural scientist in the manner in which they assign importance to the problems they find. Problems, for them, become important to the extent that people are legitimately concerned about them. If possible, it is objectively neater if people's concerns are based on a certain kind of legitimacy, say, economic cost. I recently served as chairman of a National Academy of Sciences committee on how to get more USA drivers to wear their safety belts (apparently only one in seven does so at the present time). It was only natural for the committee members to try to show that the concern about safety belts was legitimate, and to many of them the proof of the legitimacy was the economic cost to the nation and its industries of the failure of drivers to wear them. Apparently, basing legitimacy on economic costs seemed to most of the committee members a calmer, more thoughtful approach than simply getting angry at the carelessness of people who got themselves and others killed by their failure to wear the belts.

Now the reason, I think, that these planners want to formulate the problem first, is that such a step provides feasible boundaries to the ethical issues, which need no further defense, i.e., which stop the conversation. "All will agree that needless waste of economic resources is highly undesirable, and that remedies must be found to reduce or eliminate the waste." The keen interest the USA has taken in productivity is just another example of this kind of thinking.

I don't believe I've ever seen a textbook in operations research or planning that did not state that the first task was to formulate the problem, including the text that I and a number of other authors wrote in 1957.[10] We are to search among the insect population for those that do the most damage, and then make models and gather data to tell us how to minimize the harm they create. By behaving in this manner, we also reduce to a minimum our responsibility to defend our planning activities on an ethical basis.

One final example. Outside Vienna in the town of Laxenburg is the International Institute of Applied Systems Analysis (IIASA). It was founded by the USA and the USSR to provide systems analysts with the opportunity to study peaceful problems of the world, and now has seventeen member nations from both the western and eastern blocks. IIASA is a good example of the kind of planning I've been describing; indeed, it has been organized by "problem areas," without any explicit justification: energy, food, human settlements, etc. Its Charter announces that it will address the problems of peace in the world, as though the problems of peace could readily be separated from the problems of war. Perhaps a very naive political question is to ask an Institute devoted to studying human systems to explain what kind of system the

---

10.   C. West Churchman, Russell L. Ackoff, E. Leonard Arnoff, et al. *Introduction to Operations Research*, (N.Y.: John Wiley, 1957).

Institute is, and to justify its existence or nonexistence on the basis of
its reply.

One takes a step from thought towards wisdom if one asks thought
itself to examine one of its most precious assumptions. To do this, suppose we don't let thought end the ethical conversation. Suppose we ask
it to explore in a "what if" mode for awhile. What if problems are not
like insects that populate a volume? What if the so-called problems are
all tightly interconnected, every problem being an aspect of all the
others?

I can ask one of my mentors, Anaxagoras, to illustrate this speculation. In the sixth and fifth centuries B.C., many brilliant Greek
physicists were asking about the nature of the reality we humans inhabit.
They proceeded in their inquiry by the method of analysis, which means
breaking down reality to irreducible elements, and then showing how the
elements can be used to explain all the complicated objects we observe:
tables, buildings, grass, lakes, mountains, etc. The process is very similar
to the method that systems analysis uses in building its models out of
"elementary" variables. Water, or water-air-earth-fire, or other possibilities were explored by these "pre-Socratic" thinkers. Anaxagoras took a
nonanalytic approach. He said, in effect, that no matter how far one
goes in breaking an object down to parts and subparts and sub-subparts,
the resulting piece of reality still contains everything: "in every thing is
everything." He did add one strange exception: not every thing has a
"rational principle" ("nous"), a point I'll return to in a moment.

Hence, the "what if" I'd like to explore is this: in every so-
called problem of humanity is to be found all other problems, no matter how minutely we analyze.

We can also add Anaxagoras' exception: in every problem is to
be found all other problems, except the rational principle. The "rational
principle" I take to mean the ethical principles that justify any approach
we take to better the social condition. That is, we need an "unbounded"
systems approach which must include a study of the ethics of humanity,
not within a problem area, but universally.

I should now add that the speculation I'm trying to design does
not exclude problems from the reality of the planner. Indeed, all planning begins with a problem. There is a close analogy here with the

beginning of Kant's *Critique of Pure Reason,* where Kant says "That all knowledge begins with experience, there can be no doubt." The unwary are apt to conclude "here's just another empiricist," except that Kant immediately goes on to tell us that knowledge must contain more than experience, e.g., nonexperiential universals. By analogy, my speculation says that all planning begins with a problem, but should not be confined to the problem statement. Furthermore, the beginning should not be a clear problem formulation, but rather should be an utterance of moral outrage. John Dewey once said that problems arise from "felt needs," but I think this is much too mild a statement. Problems arise for all of us personally when we see people being badly treated by other people; for example, helpless people treated in ways that arouse our moral feelings. One very sad aspect of a great deal of planning research is that the roots of the "Request-for-Proposals" are cut off at the very start; no wonder the plant withers and dies as proposals, interim and final reports are written.

For example, the problem of world-wide starvation is morally outrageous: it is morally outrageous that a species that has the resources to feed every member adequately and the intelligence to do so, in fact lets millions starve. But my speculation says that this problem should unfold into other problems of national politics, of world trade, of religion, of culture, etc. To try to define "starvation" carefully at the outset tends, I think, to prevent the unfolding, so that we planners remain stuck in the bounded problem region.

I will be illustrating all this in the next chapter, because to me there is no doubt that future generations are both helpless and being treated badly by a great many live humans today.

I should also add to the picture the idea that moral outrage does not judge the importance of problems in terms of numbers, either numbers of people or numbers of dollars. Recently, I was asked to write a piece about Locke, California, a town that was founded by the Chinese railroad workers of a couple of generations ago. Now there are only about twenty of the eighty-year-old men left. The state planners want to make Locke into a state historical monument for tourists, while a developer from Hong Kong wants to make it a kind of "Chinese

Disneyland". No one had asked the old men what they wanted, until a young man decided to make a video tape of the town. The old men wanted to be left alone to die in their town with no tourists and no re-design. One could not help feeling moral outrage that the lives of the old men were being treated as means only by the state planners and the developer. No matter that there are "only" twenty old men who will live for "only" five to ten years more. The moral outrage is still quite strong. I might add, of course, that if the numbers were very high, as in the case of murdered Jews in World War II, or starving kids in the world today, then moral outrage may be accompanied by moral astonishment and horror.

The point is that the problem of Locke will eventually unfold into the larger and larger systems problem, to the problems of the aged in our society, to the problems of resources for all the needy, and so on. The beginning, the image that starts us on the pathway of understanding, need not be very "large" at all.

The speculation I am trying to depict has an awesome quality which is caught by the etymology of the verb "to decide," the meaning of which comes from the Latin verb "to cut." A decision cuts away all the other possible threads of human life, most of them never to occur in the reality of one person's lifetime. This seems patently true to most of us as we reflect in aging on our decisions about marriage, children, jobs, education, friends, and enemies. Imagination has no difficulty in showing us what "it might have been," and as imagination performs its task of designing a film about our other possible lives, mood accom-panies the film with feelings such as "Thank God it never happened," "What if it had happened?" or "What joy there would have been."

The awe arises from the reflection that we humans were born into a world where decisions to act cut off the realization of all sorts of possible designs of human living, finally and forever. Speculative his-tory can draw upon this reflection as a rich source: a history where Lincoln decided not to go to Ford's Theatre, or Caesar not to cross the Rubicon, or Hitler to invade England early in World War II.

Now it is perfectly reasonable for thought to argue that all de-cisions we humans believe we make are not real. Indeed, thought of the past had some pretty strong arguments for the position that "decision," in the sense of willfully cutting off possibilities, is illustory. For a rationalist like Spinoza, who believed that all reality is perfection, the existence of an event in reality is like a theorem in geometry. One cannot decide to make triangles with interior angles summing to less than two right angles. In the same manner, one cannot decide whom to marry. For Spinoza, all events are inferences from the perfection of God. Leibniz, who has much in common with present day operations researchers, said in effect that God built a gigantic model (e.g., a non-linear program), which described possible universes, and since his God was a perfect computer, He could use the model to calculate the design of an optimal universe, which He then implemented (having no politics to prevent implementation).

The end of the nineteenth century witnessed a severe battle between "mechanists" and "vitalists" about the reality of freedom of choice. The fight was really between some leading physicists and some philosophical biologists; the latter, e.g., Henri Bergson, wanted to use a nonphysical "vital force" to define life. But the physicists realized that the vitalists were ruining their game because in the physics of the nineteenth century, the aim was to state the laws of nature without exception. If the vitalist won out, the poor physicist would have to state the Second Law of Thermodynamics with the added clause "except when vital forces are around."

Today, the fight has virtually disappeared. Very few planners or managers even think about determinism at all. I'll cite two intellectual reasons and one humanistic why this is so. First, most philosophers have come to the conclusion that the universe was not created by a perfect designer, nor does it operate according to perfect laws. One suspects at times that Erich Jantsch's enthusiasm for his evolutionary principle may be leading the way back to a Spinozistic viewpoint, with evolution as the perfect force instead of deduction. But I found in my friendship with Erich that every time I tried to interpret his work in the context of the history of philosophy, he most emphatically denied the interpretation.

Second, we logicians have discovered that contraries (propositions that cannot both be true) exist only in the context of a given language and its rules of sentence-formation and deduction. In broader languages, the contrariness disappears. Thus Euclid's famous Parallel Postulate is

false in so-called non-Euclidian plane geometrics, but both Euclidian
plane geometry and non-Euclidian plane geometry hold true for surfaces
in three dimensional geometry (where "straight line" is the shortest path
between two points on the surface). In the same manner, Singer [11]
showed how in a more general language of science than either the
language of mechanics or biology, one could legitimately say that all
events are determined and that some events are freely chosen; "the
world behaves in accordance with deterministic (including statistical)
laws" and "the world in part behaves in accordance with teleological
laws of choice" are *not* contraries.

For me the humanistic argument is more to the point. To say that
all human decisions are predetermined is a pure cop-out, for it removes
from humanity's concerns the responsibility of the plight of the world,
its poverty, pollution, overpopulation, and military threat. This point is
probably in the spirit of the Vickers' lectures, because he takes responsibility to be an essential part of the structure of organizations, including
nations. I'd be inclined to say that the failure of the intellect to accept
responsibility because of the intellectual argument for determinism, is
morally outrageous.

I began my discussion of an Anaxagoras' hypothesis with "what
if?" Now I'd like thought to carry the speculation into reality, because
there is an argument that convinces me that the nonbounded approach
to systems is the correct one. Indeed, the "what if" may have appeared
absurd to many people who design their lives around a multitude of problems, both little and big: what to buy to eat, what kind of shoes to wear,
whether to purchase or rent a house, whether to get married, have children,
and so on. Do all these problems contain all the rest? The answer is
"no" if we don't think about them very much, and "yes" if we try to
deliberate in depth.

In defense of the "yes," I call as witness an old and fairly small
problem of systems analysis, namely, the inventory problem. In one of
its "simplest" examples, the problem asks how many items should be
ordered by a retail store and placed on the shelf to respond adequately

---

11.   Edgar A. Singer, Jr., *Experience and Reflection* (Philadelphia, PA: University
of Pennsylvania Press, 1957).

to consumer demand. The problem is deceptively simple, because it seems to be a mere matter of the comparison of two costs: the cost of over-ordering so that unsold inventories sit unproductively on the shelf, and the cost of being out of the item when a customer is there and ready to purchase it. The simplicity fades away when we ask how we should measure the first cost. What does it cost the store to keep one thousand dollars worth of inventory on the shelf for a day? The obvious answer is this: it costs the store the amount it could have made by using the thousand dollars for money-making purposes. But this response is ambiguous, because the thousand dollars could be used in lots of ways: it could be gambled at the race track, invested in bonds or risk stocks, or used to hire a brilliant consultant for a day. The question, then, should be modified as follows: "What is the best use of the one thousand dollars?" But this question asks how a firm should best use its capital; the question is what should be the capital structure of the firm.

In other words, the "simple" problem of inventory requires for its answering the answering of what appears to be a much more complicated problem, namely, how the firm's capital should be managed. It is easy to see that the question of purchasing for inventory also requires for its answering the determination of the firm's marketing policies, since we need to know not what demand customers do make, but rather the optimal demand pattern the firm can create through pricing and advertising.

I apologize for taking you on this rather dull and tedious trip, but I've done so to make the same point as did the Anaxagoras speculation: in a problem as simple as the question of the amount to purchase for inventory is to be found all the other problems of the firm. In any specific problem one finds the connectedness to all the other problems, and it is the nature of the connectedness that is central to the planning of an organization. [12]

Despite the fact that opportunity costs are technical, nonetheless they are a reality of all our lives; they are the essence of the design of a lifetime. The most important task of management, whether management of an organization or one's life, is to be able to assess the values of lost

---

12.   A note at the end of this chapter generalizes on the point I've been trying to make.

opportunities. This is why "values" are a central topic of our conversations about living.

I think that our failure to examine and plan around connectedness accounts for the plight of the human being today. Of course, the problem is how we are going to go about the task of determining the connections. Some systems analysts want to build very large models, but I don't see how the size of the model necessarily answers the question of the determination of the "opportunity" costs I've just been discussing.

There are several interesting epistemological consequences of opportunity costing. One is that the method of analysis called reductionism completely fails, because as we pursue the question of how much the keeping of inventory on a shelf really costs, the pathway leads us, not to simpler issues, but to more and more complicated ones.

The second point is that an opportunity cost is not an empirical datum, or "fact." There's simply no way to observe it. Nor is it a mere "appearance," because it's real enough: what I sacrifice when I give up an opportunity to do x because I do y instead is a real sacrifice. Appearance and reality in the old-fashioned ontology of the centuries of philosophy simply disappear. Opportunity costs are "neither of the above."

It is reasonable enough to ask how we do in fact determine opportunity costs in practice. One answer I've already suggested and rejected: that we determine them by bounding the problem. If I go to Reno and have the opportunity of playing blackjack or craps, I can perform an expected-return analysis of these two options and select the one with the largest score. But this doesn't answer the question whether I should be in Reno in the first place.

I do know how some of our ancestors suggested we solve the larger problem: namely, by trying to understand the nature of God. A perfect intellect would have no problem with the fact that every problem of decision making, no matter how small, is connected to every other problem, no matter how large. Both Leibniz and Spinoza seem to have viewed God in this manner. But as I'll argue later on, neither seems to have asked whether a being that is simultaneously omniscient a..d omnipotent can also be perfectly benevolent.[13]   There seems to be growing evidence in

13.   G.W. Leibniz seems near to examining the question in *Discours de Metaphysique.*

political history that the more technologically powerful and knowledgeable a nation becomes, the less its benevolence with respect to the helpless people of the world.

I also realize that opportunity costs are determined by politics, by the use of political clout in getting Congress and other legislative bodies to allocate funds, or managers of firms, or hospitals, or educational institutions to support programs.

Finally, I should mention a topic of conversation I'll come back to in subsequent chapters: implementation, or the transference of thought into action. Very often, thought can generate "solutions" to some of our most pressing problems, e.g., of world malnutrition or world militarism. But thought has no idea about how these solutions can be put into action. Wisdom would have to say that no matter how thoughtful the so-called solutions, they are not solutions at all.

No doubt this first chapter raises far more questions than it begins to respond to. That is because my intellect is on the side of question-asking. I realize that there are many who believe that what we need in today's messy world are some down-to-earth, specific answers as to how we're going to feed the starving, reduce militarism, clean the environment, and increase health. We question-askers are very much afraid that, as in the past, so in the future, these very practical, realistic, feasible responses to the questions, if carried into action, will make the world worse than ever.

This is what I think I said in this chapter:

(1) The use of the human intellect to improve the human condition requires a lot of thought about ethical issues.

(2) Our ancestors can help us quite a bit in this task.

(3) We need to have an unbounded approach to planning, because bounded thought may take us down disastrous pathways.

(4) Besides, thought itself can demonstrate the reality of the connectedness between problems.

(5) Wisdom may be thought which proceeds with deep ethical concerns and an unbounded approach.

This is what I have said only a little about as yet: how can unbounded thought ever make a recommendation for action?

NOTE

It is typical of writers on "decision making" to depict a decision maker as one who is confronted by a set of alternative "actions," A_1, A_2, . . . , A_n, which have varying degrees of effectiveness with respect to a set of relevant objectives which may be produced over a given time segment. In the case of gambling, e.g., slot machines, the actions are morphologically defined in that, within a range, one simply activates an energy source, or else does not, and the outcome is entirely up to the laws of nature. But in most real management decisions, the alternative actions are teleologically defined: invest x dollars, fire or hire y workers, build z units of capacity, etc. Each of these choices demands a set of management designs, and each so-called "choice" (A_i) requires an optimal design. This requirement takes us into a different system (finance, personnel, engineering, etc.). Thus, to define the problem in terms of alternative strategies is to enlarge the problem and break through systems barriers.

2

FUTURE GENERATIONS:
HUMANITY'S INVARIANCES

In the last chapter I said that it would be a good thing if the systems planner's germination was moral outrage and not just a mild felt need. In other words, I do not think we should view the major problems of the world today with calm objectivity. We shouldn't first ask ourselves for a precise and operational definition of malnutrition. We should begin with "kids are starving in great numbers, damn it all!" In the case of the plight of future generations, the grounds for moral outrage seem plentiful indeed.

But now I want to bring another character into the conversation, namely, Hope. I'll use St. Paul's way of describing hope, namely, that we can will ourselves to hope and hope operates without evidence; or rather operates when the evidence is all to the contrary of what we hope.

Consider, now, future generations, and in particular what President Carter, in his farewell address, put at the top of his list of the nation's problems: nuclear warfare. During the "safer" days of World War II, I worked in a USA Army Ordnance Laboratory. Some of my colleagues in metallurgy were busy trying to develop an armor plate that would resist penetration by any known bullet. Nearby, not surprisingly, was a laboratory where researchers were trying to develop a bullet that would penetrate any known armor. This piece of research insanity had infinite funding. I suspect the penetrators will win out; it somehow seems easier to develop a nuclear bomb that will find everybody than to invent a shelter that will be safe no matter what the bomb.

Of course, an aspect of the arms race is designed secrecy, so that few of us have any kind of accurate information regarding the power of the safeguards. At the end of one of the films depicting the devastation of a future nuclear holocaust, we are told by "experts" from the Department of Defense that nothing of the kind could ever happen, but we are not told why we should believe this piece of assurance. In the case of pollution of the environment by nonmilitary pollutants, we are fed a lot of data, a lot of conflicting data, to be sure. But at least the debate seems to be in the open. But the pollution by military pollutants may be an order of magnitude greater, and growing all the time, so that even without a nuclear war it may be exceedingly dangerous to the next generations of our children and grandchildren. Thus we can see the strange disconnectedness of the military and nonmilitary subsystems in our society; we of the nonmilitary sector struggle hard to keep the environment as clean as possible, even though the military sector may be polluting it twice as much as ever before.

The nonmilitarists act as though the military sector were unreal, because we ordinary people have no way of using our thought processes adequately when it comes to thinking about the military system. Recently, my daily paper reported a "Reagan victory" because 150 million dollars had been cut from some welfare program. On the same page, the news was that the Secretary of Defense was requesting an additional 30 billion dollars. Somehow, we are led to think that ordinary, everyday living dollars are not like military dollars, the latter being minted on special, secret military machines. Shades of the Wild, Wild West!

To return to the example at the end of the last chapter, most of military equipment goes into inventory; it serves virtually no economic function except the wages of those who guard and maintain it. As every inventory control expert knows, one of the prominent costs of holding inventory is the obsolescence cost, a very high cost in markets where styles change rapidly (you're apt to get caught with thousands of flare-out pants just when everybody wants to go back to stove-pipes). Military markets must change in fantastically fast and often unpredictable ways. I just don't see how the military could have anything like a plan or model for reasonably long-term inventory control. It follows from what was said in the last chapter that the military also have no real management control of their system: no one is "running it"; not the President, Chiefs of Staff, Congress, UN, etc. But we can all hope that there will be an end to all this nonsense, a time of human peace.

Now there is one aspect of future generations that seems unbounded: we have no adequate way of assigning a priority to them. Your grandchildren you may be able to see, but that hardly qualifies them for more importance than those of the sixth — or sixtieth — generation. But we may be able to say this much in comparing the next generation's plight with the plight of the sixth generation from now: since we are bequeathing to both a deadly threat of total destruction which is out of control, the probability that there will be a sixth generation which lives like our own is much smaller than the probability that the next generation will live normal lives. I hope this estimate is wrong.

I now would like to turn to the methodology of planning. If the first step is a feeling of moral outrage, or even, as in the case of the current military system, moral horror, what then? In the last two decades, the answer in the public domain has been civil dissent, which has almost always been followed by a counter moral outrage. Thus, in 1964, the UC Berkeley campus erupted when the students felt moral outrage at the way they were being treated by the administration and faculty. Among other things, they sat-in in the main administration building. This action produced huge moral indignation among the taxpayers in Orange County who told the governor of the state to "get those brats out of the building our taxes built."

I have a personal bias against this dissent methodology that follows moral outrage although it may in fact be the best we humans can invent. My bias is based on a faith in the human intellect. The design of my philosophical life is based on an examination of the following question: is it possible to secure improvement in the human condition by means of the human intellect? The verb "to secure" is (for me) terribly important, because, as I said in the first chapter, problem solving often appears to produce improvement, but the so-called "solution" often makes matters worse in the larger system (e.g., the many food programs of the last quarter century may well have made world-wide starvation even worse than no food programs would have done). The verb "to secure" means that in the larger system over time the improvement persists.

I have to admit that the philosophical question is much more difficult than my very limited intellect can handle. I don't know what "human condition" and "human intellect" mean, though I've done my best to tap the wisdom of such diverse fields as depth psychology, economics, sociology, anthropology, public health, management science, education, literature, and history. But to me the essence of philosophy is to pose serious and meaningful questions that are too difficult for any of us to answer in our lifetimes. Wisdom, or the love of wisdom, is just that: thought likes solutions, wisdom abhors them.

For me, therefore, moral outrage is to be followed by the calm of intellectual inquiry. The design of such inquiry is based on the question "What can be done about it?" To use a term very familiar to planners, the next step in planning methodology is the examination by the human intellect of the question of implementation. You will note, I hope, that the next step is *not* a careful formulation of the problem. The residue of moral outrage is that something is terribly wrong and there is a real need for action that will reduce the wrong. My argument with nutritional researchers is that they seem to have taken their mission to be one of measuring malnutrition in the starving villages of the world. To me, the moral meaning seems to be much more to the point: people are very hungry, without any real prospect of easing the hunger pangs, and they need not be hungry at all. What can be done about this?

Before designing action with respect to future generations, I have let thought address one critical issue. If we are planning for those who live today, we can at least obtain their help in deciding what objectives we should plan to realize. But given the vast changes in life style which history demonstrates, how can we tell what people will want a century from now? A century ago middle and upper class people in affluent societies did not want automobiles in great numbers, cared nothing about the quality of TV programs worried a lot about infectious diseases, and (in England and the USA) were morally stuffy and generally indifferent about the plight of the poor. The question for thought is whether human societies change so radically that we could not possibly plan for the future beyond a very limited number of years.

There has been quite a bit of discussion about change in the Gaither Lectures. At times, Jantsch seems to be saying that literally everything changes, until one realizes that the principle of evolution itself is invariant. Some physicists, like Dirac, have speculated on the possibility that the so-called physical constants may be shifting, but, of course, if they do change, one would like to know the laws expressing the change, and these laws would have to have universal constants that either don't change; or themselves change in accordance with other laws, etc.

In any event, without getting into the subtleties of absolute invariances, I think it safe to say that my eight Gaither predecessors all accepted relatively long-term invariances. Hitch presupposed that for a very long time to come we're going to have to worry about the effectiveness of our administration of the military system. Schultze accepted the fact that government budgets are going to be around for a long time. Rivlin thought that the need for large-scale social programs is prevalent. For Macy, the fight to bring culture to the masses will not, or should not, be soon over. Vickers accepted the fact that weakening of responsibility in human organizations is a long-run concern. For Jantsch, autopoiesis is eternal. Simon, who dealt explicitly with the subject of future generations, believed that one invariant of their value systems was the need for many options, and I believe he would add "options of a high quality." I infer from the spirit of Raiffa's lectures that the need for well-designed negotiation and arbitration processes will be with us for centuries to come.

For me the value of the "humanity within" is not only an invariant, but a sacred one. This implies a moral law with respect to future generations: we should undertake to design our socieites and their environments so that the people of the future will be able to design their lives in ways that express their own humanity.

Now I'm ready to consider plans for action: one that has already taken place, one that is seriously contemplated, and one that is only being talked about. The first is conservation, by which I mean that this generation attempts to conserve some aspects of nature in its present state, without consuming it for our own benefit. Two examples come to mind: the Endangered Species Act of the USA and the USA's preservation of wilderness areas which, in the main, are not used for recreational purposes.

The Endangered Species Act empowers the executive branch of our government, and specifically the Fish and Wildlife Service, to place species it deems to be either threatened or endangered on a published list. Furthermore, the agency is to take actions (such as stopping the building of a dam) it considers essential to turn the trend around so that the species is no longer threatened or endangered. The story of the saving of the whooping crane is both heroic and hilarious. This is a species which at one time numbered in the hundreds of thousands, and within the last decade had dropped to eighteen. It seems now on the way back to a number that will make it safe for survival if our next-door neighbors, the Canadians, behave themselves. At one point, a biologist roomed with a mamma crane, one expects in purity; at another, helicopters roared around the migrating cranes to keep them from landing in a polluted lake. (This crane is a stubborn bird which landed anyway, no doubt muttering, "what are they up to now?") In Aransas, Texas, the winter home of the crane, the wildlife refuge people have built a tower from which visitors can look down on the cranes. I asked the director what happened when the cranes, who are very independent, didn't show up. "Oh," he said, "that doesn't matter. As one woman said, 'it's enough just to see where the cranes have stood.'"

The Endangered Species Act is now about nine years old. It can be defended on the grounds that our generation has no right to act as our grandfathers did, by wantonly slaying buffalo, egrets, and many other species. We should be caretakers of the species so that those to come will be able to express their humanity by sharing nature with non-human species. It is a fairly expensive act, which, I think, cannot be defended by benefit-cost measures. It, itself, is endangered. We as a nation have become obsessed with the idea of reducing inflation, and equally obsessed with the notion that this needs to be done by reducing government expenditures. The Endangered Species Act is a duck sitting in a barrel for the obsessive types.

Nonetheless, I believe the Act was an act of wisdom, because it combined thought and a religious attitude towards nature. Wisdom always has a religious dimension, i.e., the holding of something precious as also being sacred.

The battle over conservation vs. recreation continues to wage in the government. The conservationists must answer the question, "When shall the wilderness lands be made accessible?" The recreationists have to show that lands where people go will not be so changed that the species (including plants) can't survive.

The two examples do show that there is some major concern about what this generation can do to the lives of those to come, probably more concern than humans have ever shown before. But we also have created a world of military threat where "wilderness" no longer has its pristine meaning: the aftermath of a nuclear holocaust could be just as devastating in a wilderness as in a city.

The second course of action is similar to the first, but its intent is to leave the set of options for future generations as broad as possible. When in the 1780's Bentham was designing his pleasure-pain calculus for government planners, he listed all the considerations that planners need to attend to in regard to the total pleasure minus pain that a policy or law might produce. Included in the list is "propinquity," or "how soon?" It is common sense for any of us to say that given the choice between a pleasure now and the same pleasure a year from now, we should choose the former since we may not be around at all a year from now. (Of course, some people may get all their kicks from anticipation, so that, as usual, common sense may not be right.) Economics refined Bentham's common sense by saying that receiving a dollar today is worth more than receiving a dollar a year from now, because today's dollar can yield additional wealth over the year. The amount that a well-designed investment yields is called the "discount rate." (I should point out that the determination of the appropriate discount rate runs into the same connectedness problems as does the determination of opportunity costs: it carries us into the whole financial system of a person, corporation, or government).

The same idea applies to pains and costs: it's better to delay a pain or a cost. In the case of a future cost compared to a present one, we accrue for a year the wealth we can gain from a dollar we don't have to spend now. Hence a positive discount rate says that costs occurring in the future are less serious than costs occurring now, and, indeed, there is a point in the future beyond which the costs don't matter.

When we turn our attention to such matters as strip mining and nuclear plants, and the values of future generations, neither Bentham's nor the economists' considerations appear appropriate. Suppose, for example, we were to plot the economic benefit minus costs of nuclear plants we have built in this country against time. Within a few decades the line will dip below the time axis: all that will be left will be the cost of nuclear waste and the cost of an obsolete plant. Dare we say to those who for centuries will have to live with the costs: "look, we got a lot of energy out of the plants during our lifetime, and the discount rate for us made the future of the plants virtually irrelevant?" As a student of a morality based on the moral law of never treating the humanity of another, no matter in what future era, as means only, I can only say we dare not say anything of the kind.

A number of long-range planners have seen a way out of the embarrassment of assigning positive discount rates to future events of the next generations. The method consists of including a trust fund as a part of the cost of a present development that will only have negative benefits to future generations. The interest accruing from the trust fund would be used to pay future generations, e.g., to pay them for protecting themselves from the harms of nuclear waste. Perhaps the fund should be large enough to give them a bit extra for their trouble.

I call this rather arrogant suggestion a battle between "willingness to pay" and "equity." I've used it[14] to illustrate the policy of killing off a species like the egret in the swamps of Florida so that ladies on Fifth Avenue could wear egret-feathered hats in the Easter Parade. I concluded that payment to future generations for the lost opportunities this generation creates in order to satisfy its desires is probably all right for a weak utilitarian ethics but all wrong for an ethics of equity. Part of the "humanity within us" is our connectedness to other species, as I've suggested above. To accept payment for the loss of this connectedness is immoral. To propose to a future generation that it accept payment for our immorality is also immoral.

---

14.   See Part II, Chapter 5, "Willingness to Pay and Morality: A Study of Future Values."

I must conclude that I can find no "economic" method for planning for future generations, if the economic method is to use a utilitarian ethics only. Of course, there is nothing to stop an economist from writing moral- ity into the constraint equations of a mathematical model, as long as he doesn't use the moral constraints to calculate the cost of being moral. The evils of morality cannot be costed in an equity morality like Kant's.

On the third possible action program for future generations, I shall be brief. In a democratically designed pluralistic society, we believe that the proper design of decision making entails the right of each citizen to express his wishes regarding his representatives, and, to the extent possible, his wishes regarding the laws that regulate his society. Democracy is thus a process of interacting constituencies.

Ever since Plato in the *Republic* wrote his indictment of democracy, systems philosophers have had to play out the dialectic of a rational so- ciety vs. a democratic society. There can surely be no guarantee that the resultant decision produced by conflicting constituencies is rational in any of the historically accepted meanings of rationality. We planners, in our proposed interventions to feed people, design developments, and the like, are acting like Plato's philosopher kings. We try to soften our arrogance by saying that the community must decide: we planners facili- tate their decisions by providing the right kind of information, say. But, then, we do intervene from a superior position. We really have no good answer to the question of intervention, simply because we have no rational way of judging constituency-based decision making to be correct.

Furthermore our thought-process finds what to us is a devastating weakness in constituency-based decision making: future generations have no way of becoming constituencies, no way of expressing their needs and wants. One could say exactly the same thing about past generations. Our culture is so oriented to the living or those who will live, that we have lost the sacred obligation to worship our ancestors and their needs and wants. There is no reason why the event called death should cancel all rights to be a member of a constituency for present and future decisions of society.

Now, imagination suggests a response to this complaint of the ra- tional mind, namely, that we create among the living the two constitu- encies of the future and the past generations. We can even use the present constituencies to elect members to both. These "representatives" could serve in legislative bodies, or in public forums of various kinds. Like any other constituency, they can form alliances that increase their political power. When present constituencies seem bent on destroying the environment or a great tradition, either or both past and future constituencies can create the political atmosphere of crisis, in order to stop the move towards the neglect of their ideals.

I should pause here to comment on the quality of each of the three examples, and specifically the aesthetics of each of them. To me, the Endangered Species Act has a high aesthetic appeal, because it has a radiance about it. In Part II, Chapter 6, I have argued that the Act is also religious in character.

On the other hand, the action of using a trust fund to pay future generations for the devastation we bequeath to them seems to me to be highly unaesthetic and to lack radiance completely.

The political constituency action, although strongly moral in its image, is not yet either aesthetic or unaesthetic, because its quality will depend largely on its design. If the constituencies turn out to be very weak politically, then the action will be very unaesthetic, just one more example of the horrible way we are treating both past and future humans.

These aesthetic appreciations of plans lead me to a speculation. As the first chapter indicates, the use of unbounded reason by thought leads to an almost endless unfolding of the boundaries of a system, so that action seems impossible. But it may be the better part of wisdom to let aesthetics be a guide to action. In other words, if an action with respect to future generations seems to have a strong aesthetic appeal, one should stop further thought and act. It's to be noted that this policy makes morality and aesthetics (the good and the beautiful) allies in the struggle to improve the human condition.

Suppose now we return to thought and ask it to converse on the three actions. Thought's first reaction is that in an unbounded systems approach, action may very well be wrong, i.e., lead to failure. There is surely a good argument for saying that the Endangered Species Act was passed long before our American society could tolerate it, and since it was, its chances of ever being renewed after it is repealed are very small. I've already questioned the legitimacy of the "trust fund" to pay future

Future Generations
27

generations for our selfishness. And it may very well be the case that
future and past constituencies are utterly unrealistic.

The point, to be elaborated in the next chapter, is that action
leads us into the domain of success and failure. Of course, thought alone
may fail. I'll use my favorite hobby, chess, to illustrate the point I'm
trying to make. After you pass through a standard opening like the Sicil-
ian you have to let thought take over because you're "beyond the book."
You start conversing with yourself, somewhat as follows: "I could move
my knight to there, and he'd move his bishop there, and I could then
move a pawn there, but that's no good because he'd win my queen." So
far thought has led to a failure, but unless you're playing by a clock,
no harm has been done; thought can go back and try another tack. But
once you decide to move, i.e., go into action, then success and failure
become crucial, and your mood is apt to change drastically. Indeed,
your opponent may use a little psychology, and by responding quickly
may try to give you the impression that he's got it all figured out, and
you've consequently failed.

So thought needs to explore in greater depth the domain of success and failure, and this will be the topic of the next chapter's
conversation.

But thought now introduces, as is its wont, a much more general
question about action: to what extent have the collective actions of
mankind really mattered? Put otherwise, is there such a thing as progress
in human affairs? The question may seem naive because it appears to
be so broad and abstract. If we bound the question, a fantastic list of
"progressive measures" emerges: humans here and there have increased
length of life, reduced (and in the case of smallpox, eliminated) incidence
of diseases, increased years of education, increased productivity, increased
miles-per-hour in transportation, increased precision of measurements, and
so on. But, of course, one can counter each of these progressive gains
by pointing out their shadow or negative sides. We have also increased
our neglect of the elderly, increased the incidence of cancer and coro-
nary-respiratory diseases, increased the use of educational institutions
as prisons to keep the kids in control, increased the number and variety
of dangerous products, increased the death rate on highways, increased

the precision of bombings, and so on.[15]

Still, has there been over all progress in the last three centuries, say? I need to go back in history to a time when the unbounded question was taken very seriously. I take the time I have in mind to start with St. Augustine in the fifth century A.D., though its roots go back to Plato. The idea is to start by thinking through to a definition of perfection as it applies to the human condition, and thence to assessing where the real human condition is with respect to perfection, e.g., whether it is moving towards or away from the ideal. Plato tried to accomplish the first task in the *Republic* but never designed a successful assessment method for the second. Indeed, the proponents of human progress had to wait until the nineteenth century for a sound measure of progress in one domain, the acquisition of knowledge.

Meanwhile, the search for the meaning of perfection proceeded from St. Anselm down to its flowering in the seventeenth century when Descartes could say, with all the confidence of his doubting mind, that he had a clear idea of perfection. Essentially, the seventeenth century design of the idea of perfection was what I would call an "add-on" design. One first thinks of a quality which has gradations going from bad to good: bad knowledge to good knowledge, bad (weak) power to good (strong) power, etc. In the case of each of these qualities one defines a maximum. One then conjoins all the maxima on all the qualities, and the result is taken to be perfection. The seventeenth century had several questions to ask about this design method, and we in the twentieth can ask some more. Spinoza doubted that humans could understand the infinite set of attributes of God. We today would still like to know whether the set of qualities is exhaustive. Since the seventeenth century, except for time and distance, had no scales of the qualities in our sense of scale (essentially a twentieth century invention), we could question their logical right to conceptualize worst, bad, better, and best.[16]

---

15.   I should note that my question is somewhat different from the one Nesbit poses in his *The Idea of Progress*. He seems to be asking whether human progress actually exists, whereas I'm asking whether it can be designed. Hence, assessment for me is crucial, whereas for Nesbit it is not. See R. Nesbit *The Idea of Progress*.

16.   It is interesting to note that Leibniz and Spinoza had a rather modern notion of perfection in the deductive sciences: a perfect being in this domain takes no time to deduce a theorem, or, as we would say, it has a perfect algorithm and computer with zero processing time.

Finally, if you take quality a and then b, and make."a and b" out of them, as every logician knows, you have to show that "a and b" is not the empty class. Leibniz seems to have sensed this problem in his *Discours on Metaphysics.*

Nineteenth and twentieth century statistics provided us with a measure of performance in the domain of empirical science, namely, the probable error (or standard deviation) of a measurement method. This measure informs us about the accuracy of our empirical findings. As far as I know, E. A. Singer Jr. was the only philosopher of science who appreciated the epistemological significance of the concept of a probable error. Almost all the philosophers of his time, and especially the positivists, believed in a reductionist empiricism, so that to them "verification" in empirical science meant reducing a question to the simplest sensations. For Singer, any question we address to nature must be posed in a language which permits us to estimate the probable error of the response the scientist gives to the question, e.g., the language of arithmetic. There are no simple questions we can pose to nature.

Singer also saw that the probable error alone was not enough as a measure of performance, because it makes no sense if the measurement process is out of control. The process by which independent observers in different places and times can report findings that are in statistical control is called "calibration," one of the chief businesses of the USA National Bureau of Standards. I spent a lot of time in World War II trying to calibrate measurements in physics, chemistry, and metalurgy and found it to be a very difficult task. At times, failure to calibrate reaches the level of scandal, as in the health profession and its enormous proliferation of measurements of the human body. Singer realized that a measurement method may be out of control for many reasons, and that the measurer must "sweep in" these reasons in order to make progress. He used to emphasize the need to understand the psychology of the observers. I found that the most serious obstacle was the politics of research laboratories, which simply did not want an outsider to come in and tell them how to conduct their measurements.[17]

_____

17.   One time we took a small steel bar and indented it as in a Rockwell hardness measurement. We sent the bar to some twenty laboratories, each of which had several technicians measure the length of the indentation by moving a hairline in a microscope from one vertex to the other. In no laboratory was there

I hope you'll recognize the Anaxagoras theme once more: in order
to measure the distance between two points on the surface of the earth
at a given time, one has to understand the politics of research institutions.

How different Singer's notion of progress in science is from the
notion of the reductionist empiricists! Carnap once told me that the
advent of large computers was like an answer to a life-long prayer. He
imagined a very large world computer which would continuously absorb
the empirical data of scientists around the world. At any time, a qualified scientist could query the machine about the Carnapian degree of
confirmation of a specific empirical hypothesis. I asked him how the
machine would be able to assess the quality of the data (i.e., how it
would calibrate). I don't think he had ever taken such a problem to be
relevant, because for him the data would have been reduced to its simplest
elements, I suppose. It certainly never occurred to him that some data
would never reach his machine for political reasons.

Singer himself pointed out one fascination his measure of performance creates in the mind of a speculative philosopher, namely, the relationship between the real and the ideal. The ideal for empirical measurement is a probable error or zero. Since the language of Singer's
measurement method always permits the addition of another decimal
place the probable error can never be zero. But the real distance "exists" at any moment of time. [18] Hence, the ideal and the real are one
and the same.

Singer also sensed that his measure creates two images of the world
of progress. One is the image of "success." The probable error of the
method of measuring the velocity of white light in a vacuum was at
one time in the eighteenth century several thousand km./sec., and today
it is less than 0.1 km./sec. Bishop Berkeley in the eighteeneth century
could say quite seriously that distances less than one thousandth of an

---

a significant difference between technicians in the lab. But there was a real difference between laboratories, one of them reporting a hardness of about the hardness of lead, and another the hardness of the hardest of known steels. Evidently,
each lab had its own "inner culture." To bring about calibration, one had to understand something about cultural anthropology!

18.   There is a confusion here which involves the language of the Heisenberg
"indeterminacy" principle, which puts a limit on the reduction of the probable
errors of two physical attributes of a body. I've done my best to clear up what
I believe to be a linguistic confusion in my Introduction to Singer's *Experience
and Reflection,* University of Pennsylvania Press, 1959.

inch did not "exist," because no one could possibly perceive them.
Today we can measure distances far smaller than a large thousandth
of an inch. I was part of an experiment after World War II where
we photographed events that took a microsecond to occur. Today,
such events take quite a "long" time.

The other image of the world of scientific progress sees it as a
"failure," because if the world permits the continuation of science as
it has in the past century, our measurement methods will appear quite
crude to a future generation a century from now. There is no way we
can possibly say that our progress is very good, when compared to
what has to be done. Such an image will become part of the topic of
the next chapter.

But there is one aspect of Singer's measure of progress that he
recognized could constitute its complete inadequacy. The history of
modern science has elevated precision to the pinnacle of its ideals.
But this may have been a mistaken strategy. Management scientists
have claimed that their models enable them to be far more precise than
any other researchers into management can attain with their essays written in vague English. To this, their academic enemies have pointed out
that the models are often wrong because they leave out critical aspects
that can't be quantified. I'd put it somewhat differently. The models
are wrong because they make value assumptions which are wrong: the
assumed values are those of people who should not be the top priority
clients of the system. In any event, not only are the models wrong,
but they are precisely wrong. If you are the intended victim, you'd
just as soon have a pursuer whose aim is imprecise.

Singer recognized that perfect precision was only one aspect of
the ideal, and proceeded to map the domains of human social ideals.
Besides precision, there is the ideal of production and distribution,
which are somehow measured by the ability of people in a society to
satisfy their wishes by the best means. Along with these must go education, which aims at the ideal of each person's knowing how best to
use the resources available.

Of course, a society in which everyone was pretty adept in getting what they want would be chaotic, to say the least, since some
would want what others have without paying them. Hence, there must

be the ideal of cooperation, which Singer thought he could observe on occasion in the scientific community. A scientist, intent on discovering some fact of nature, may, if he is successful, increase the chances of another scientist's discovering *his* fact. In general, if when A pursues his goal, he thereby increases B's chance of obtaining B's goal, then A cooperates with B. A society in which each member cooperates with all the others in a perfect way is the cooperative ideal.

There is one more ideal in Singer's idealism that I'll talk about in the next chapter: the ideal of dissatisfaction, or a restless society.

I have two questions that bother me about Singer's idealism. The first is whether his concept of cooperation is adequate, and in particular whether it catches Kant's meaning of equity. I believe Singer thought it did, and for many years so did I. But I can see now that two people could cooperate very well in Singer's sense, but not have the least concern about the other's "humanity within." To relate to others by treating their humanity as an end-in-itself is a very subtle task. St. Paul expressed the spirit of the task quite well in Romans, 12: "For as we have many members in one body, and all members are not the same office: So we, being many, are one body in Christ, and every one members one of another." There seems to be all the difference in the world between my helping you satisfy your desires, and my regarding you as part of me. It's the same theme I've repeated before, between a utilitarian ethics of want-satisfaction, and the ethics of equity based on human relationships. I don't think Singer caught the essence of Kant's idealism.

My second question takes me back to the idea of perfection. Singer, too, used an "add-on" method: his ideal (i.e., perfection of mankind) was perfect science-education *and* perfect production-distribution *and* perfect cooperation *and* perfect dissatisfaction. I must ask whether the result is an entity that not only cannot be approximated but also cannot exist for humanity. I have no logical objections to it, but there seems to be almost overwhelming evidence that nations which advance on the science-production front become more and more decadent with respect to cooperation, whether in Singer's or Kant's sense. Such nations have the gall to call themselves "developed" and to call the less affluent ones "developing." How dare a nation which threatens to blow up the world call itself "developed"? As one African gentleman once said to me, "we are developed; you are over-developed." To me, it seems as though the human ideal must include cooperation, but the evidence is either that it cannot, or else we simply don't understand at this time how it possibly can. Thought fails to find a justification for its idea of perfection.

Of course, I sense the theological significance of this failure of thought. It's shocking enough to think that "God is dead" is a possibility, but that seems mild compared to the thought that God is impossible. My ancestors begin shouting, and above the din I can hear Descartes and Calvin cry out, "Who is this brat at Berkeley?"

But, of course, I hope this is not the end of the matter. I hope we can find a much more suitable role for perfection than it had when it was fixed without change.

There is another way to express thought's failure. Over the years I have advocated and still do advocate "ideal planning," along with several others and most especially Russell Ackoff. A simple analogy may help. Suppose a house you intend to inhabit is in terrible shape. The plumbing doesn't work, some of the floor boards are weak, some rooms are too small, the whole thing needs re-painting, and so on. You could approach the matter in two ways, as the first chapter suggests. You could ask yourself, "what is the most important thing to fix first?" Once that problem has been named, you ignore the rest for the time being and solve that one. This might be called the "housekeeping" approach to planning (some operations researchers refer to themselves as society's plumbers). Or, you could use some time for reflection and ask, "What is an ideal house for me to live in?" and then ask: "What are possible pathways that would take this house closer to the ideal, i.e., what are the things that are currently blocking my way towards the ideal?"

You are likely to find that the two approaches yield different priorities. The housekeeping approach might send you into fixing the plumbing first. The second might say, "The ideal house is one that provides both the opportunity of community-sharing and privacy." The inference might then be that the present design of the rooms is the biggest roadblock: why should we live uncomfortably in a house with perfect plumbing?

But I've found that the design of an ideal is no simple matter. I teach a seminar which is taken by a number of MBA's. Many of them have criticized the existing MBA program, so I've encouraged them to design an ideal MBA curriculum. I'd have to say that they haven't really done too well. For one thing, they've been in school so long that they can't even imagine a curriculum without ten-week long courses.

At one time I found myself complaining about the way the University conducts its affairs. Since one of my complaints was about the amount of esoteric knowledge we create and teach, I decided to design an exoteric "ideal" university. I tore down the walls and made the whole of Berkeley into a university. The core of my university was a Learning Center with no experts, a place where everyone could share their learning experiences with other members of the university. At the Learning Center one learned whether to join the university, where to seek exoteric knowledge and how to create more of it, and finally when to leave. (Some never got the message to leave; they were called "faculty.") [19]

How could I show that mine was a perfectly designed university? I couldn't. For one thing, the theme of connectedness makes me admit that such an exoteric university in a society which operates the way ours does would never work. For another, the politics of the Learning Center might well be a disaster.

The conclusion thought must make is that we don't know how to design an ideal in imagination. We don't even know whether a proposed ideal, like Singer's, is an "approximation" to perfection, or a closer approximation than some existing system. Again, we may have to appeal to our aesthetic sense, not our thoughtful assessment: ideal systems must appear radiant.

Of course, thought can say that there is such a thing as "better" if not "best." Some real systems appear to be so evil that imagination has no difficulty in designing improvement. But evil is just about as illusive as perfection. Hence, I'd like to close with one more reflection. Carl Jung proposed that every one of us has a "shadow" side. No matter how saintly, kind, and benevolent someone may appear, if you enter

---

19.   See Part II, Chapter 7.

into an exploration of his or her psyche you will discover the shadow, the evil that lies lurking in the dark corners.

I'd like to apply Jung's theory to my experience in trying to design ideals: in every ideal design, no matter how good it may appear to be, there lurks an evil aspect. Now, I can really hear the complaints from the peanut gallery. In this era of the human story there are countless heroes and heroines who are proposing either perfect or much better designs of educational and health institutions. They wouldn't really like to hear that in all their lovely reforms, no matter how appealing, there is a hidden evil.

Thought has failed in its attempt to create the idea of perfection. But this is not the end of the matter. Ever reflective thought must ask what failure means. Is it the end, or is it a beginning? Could it be a kind of success?

This is what I think I said in this chapter:

(1) Hope needs to be brought into the conversation.

(2) Our very prevalent lack of concern for future generations is morally outrageous. We are so concerned about defending our own lives that we have created a monstrous military system that seems quite likely to destroy some future generation.

(3) Three examples of actions that demonstrate a concern for future generations were discussed: the Endangered Species Act and the wilderness conservation system, the proposal to use a trust fund in estimating the costs of a development relative to future generations, and the creation of future and past generation constituencies.

(4) Thought then asks whether there is such a thing as human progress, and decides, as did Kant and Singer, that if progress exists it must be a series of approximations towards an ideal. This reflection took me into the history of the idea of perfection and to the conclusion that thought fails in its attempt to create the design of an ideal system.

(5) The failure raises the question whether some failures may be successes.

3

SUCCESS OF FAILURE:
THE JOYS OF DISSATISFACTION

Trying. The title of this chapter may seem a bit odd until one recognizes that it expresses a truism; namely that "once you don't succeed, try, try again." To catch the theme, imagine a man trying to learn how to ride a unicycle. After a bit, you might hear him say, "I'll get the hang of this thing even if it kills me"; meaning that he's willing to go all the way to the ultimate failure in order to succeed.

Note that in general one could not determine that someone was trying to do something unless the one trying fails; perfect success means a lack of "trying."

Note also that "trial and error" — or "trial and failure" — does accurately describe the process of trying, but not every failure improves performance. Indeed, many people would never get the hang of riding a unicycle, no matter how hard they tried. Somehow, the failure not only tells the trier "not that way," but it also provides hints to some triers as to a better way. Those who will never succeed probably never get these hints.

Thus the message is *not* to "try a little failure now and then; it can't hurt you." Rather, the message is to learn the quality of the failure: "Did it teach you anything, and was the amount you learned worth the failure?"

Finally, it's interesting to note that the historical root of the word "failure" is the French word "to miss the mark," an experience familiar enough to anyone trying to get the knack of shooting a gun.

Learning. "Learning" is a generalization of the word "trying," and includes not only getting the knack of some activity, but also the acquisition of intellectual knowledge. The same lesson applies; all learning involves some failure. But now the lesson is not obvious at all, at least in schools and other organizations. Many teachers tend to handle student failure by punishment or put-down. In many class-rooms, the good readers and the poor readers are separated, e.g., into two separate tables. The teacher gives far more attention to the good readers, so that the good get better and the poor get poorer. This policy often has the unfortunate consequence that the student learns nothing from his failures. He becomes aware that he shouldn't fail, but has no idea at all as to how to do this. A recent study demonstrates what many teachers already know, namely, a high correlation between failure to learn to read and student violence and vandalism. How else is the frus-trated kid to express his frustration?

The typical classroom scene is very odd. The "successful" stu-dents are rewarded, e.g., by a teacher's award to be taken home saying that Johnny has earned 100 for spelling. The failures never get the awards to take home, and are clearly third-rate citizens. Since they've not learned much from their failures, they tend to fail again and again. Furthermore, it's almost obvious how this failing policy could be changed. Suppose Billy doesn't get the hang of spelling words like "which," "what," etc., because he leaves out the soundless "h." A good teacher would call the attention of the whole class to the pecu-liarity of the "h-words" in the English language, and to the reasonable-ness of Billy's "failure." "After all," she might say, "we have words like 'wood' and 'will' that don't get dressed up with an 'h.' Why? Can we say something sensible about the h-dressers?" The result might well be increased learning by all the class. Everyone would learn from Billy's "failure." Furthermore, Billy wouldn't feel like a fool, but would recognize he'd done something important. The teacher might even give him an award to take home: " Today, Billy helped us learn something about spelling."

The same lesson can be applied to organizations. Typically, the failure of a younger member to act in accordance with the policy of the organization is received by the top brass with anger and punishment: "fire that guy!" The "failure," as in the famous case of the young man who, in an attempt to enforce the Endangered Species Act, wrote to the restaurant illegally serving rattlesnakes, may be strictly in accordance with the written rules of the organization. The response of top management should not be anger and "fire him!" but rather, "Hey, this is a reasonable act but not one we want to occur again; how can we (the organization) learn to avoid such actions? Furthermore, we're pleased that Jones drew this matter to our attention."

Indeed, we can propose a general rule for organizations with respect to learning: "reasonable failure should never be received with anger." Spinoza announced a principle very much like this. He said that the highest activity humans can attain is learning, or, in his language, understanding. To understand is to be free. He also said that we become slaves to the extent that we allow our passions to govern. Thus those who respond to the failure of others by anger are themselves slaves to their passions and learn nothing.

There is no question we live in a world of uncertainty, where managers often have to make decisions which they cannot possibly know are correct. But a lot of uncertainty in organizations is created by the managers themselves who are constantly threatening punishment (firing, no promotion, etc.) in the event of failure.

Am I being inconsistent? In the earlier chapters, I advocated "moral outrage" as a beginning. In the principle enunciated above, I did introduce the vague term "reasonable," which is supposed to stop outrage. Reasonable failure should not lead to moral outrage. I meant "reasonable" to exclude failures that have been contrived to throw a monkey wrench into the works; obviously managers have to judge whether the failure is reasonable, i.e., whether it was made with the best of intentions.

I must confess a bias in writing this chapter of the book. When I was a kid I was obliged to play football, which I hated (with a passion). Since the coach always made us awkward ones appear foolish, I thought the aim of football was to please the coach. Because I didn't like the coach at all, the game seemed to me to be utterly stupid. It was only much later that I discovered that football could be fun, especially when the goal of winning was unimportant.

I live in a world where graduate education, with its grades and required courses, often resembles football practice, or perhaps boot camp for the marines. For me, grades are about the worst invention the educational system ever made. Very few students benefit from them; for the vast majority grades interfere with real learning. It's tragic to think of the many really bright students who shy away from challenging courses and select the easy ones, just to keep up their Grade Point Average.

The mood of this chapter comes at different levels, and in my rather passionate denunciation of the angry teachers, managers, and coaches, I did not consider one aspect of organizations which may seem to justify punishment for failure. After all, failure is often in the eyes of the beholder, and if the beholder is a teacher or manager, the failure of students or employees may be regarded by the teacher or manager as their own failure. If so, they will find the fastest way to recover: punishment for the child, firing for the employee. After all, teachers and managers are very busy people with little time to spend on each case. But as every good teacher and manager comes to learn, there must be a balance between efficiency and effectiveness; only the "cost reductionists" never learn.

Error. So far, I've been talking about the role of failure in the education of younger people in our society. Now, I would like to talk in a more general vein about failure in research. One example, error, is part of the basic methodology of science. The other is the failure to attain research objectives.

The word "error" certainly sounds like an instance of failure. But scientists actually seek error. Why? One example may suffice. During World War II, I was a statistician working for Army Ordnance, mainly on improving methods of inspection. I was asked to look into the inspection procedures for testing for misfires in bullets. Misfires occur when the small primer at the back of the bullet fails to explode and hence fails to ignite the powder that drives the bullet out of the barrel. Obviously, misfires may be disastrous failures for any infantryman; also, at that time, a misfire of a calibre 50 machine gun on the wing of an airplane meant that the gun was out of action for the rest of the mission. The method of inspection of primers at the time I did my study consisted of dropping a ball on a firing pin resting on the primer's surface. The kinetic energy the falling ball produced was about equivalent to the kinetic energy of the firing pin in a gun. One hundred primers were tested, and if all fired, the entire lot of about 25,000 primers was accepted.

With a little calculation, using probability theory, I determined that a lot with as many as one percent misfires had a probability of about one-third of being accepted by this inspection procedure. But one percent misfires would have been disastrous in the field.

What I did was to reduce the kinetic energy of the falling ball, intentionally getting into the range where some up to all of the primers failed. I could thus estimate the range of kinetic energies that produced virtually all misfires up to all fires, and thus determine whether "virtually all" (99.999995%) would fire in the gun. Thus in order to learn, I'd gone into the range of error (failure). I could learn very little by testing primers when all were "successful." But I could learn a great deal when I worked in the range where many of them "failed."

Indeed, as most physical scientists know (and perhaps too few social scientists), theories are not proved or disproved by success or single failure events but by working carefully in the range of error (a theory might hold in a million cases and yet clearly be invalid in the error-range).

The lesson to be drawn here concerns the standard of "objectivity" in research. Suppose in a certain region a pollutant has been identified in a lake, and has been measured. Suppose also that it has been determined that none of a relevant species has been affected by the pollutant. Even though this fact has been well established, the fact by itself is not "objective evidence" that nothing needs to be done.

Instead, a "test of increased severity" should be used, to test the pollutant in the range where it does have an effect, and thus estimate how close the existing measure of pollution is to the "killing range."

Failure in the Research Community. Now I'd like to turn my attention to another type of failure in science, namely, the failure to find an explanation for a phenomenon, and thus failure to prevent the phenomenon (as in the case of diseases and disasters), or failure to make the phenomenon occur (as in the case of rainfall or high crop yield).

Given the complexity of the natural world, one would expect a high degree of failure of the sort just described, especially if the phenomenon is not understood very well. One might expect, therefore, that a good policy for a research community to follow would be to show a lot of patience, especially if the phenomenon is very important in the design of many human lives.

One example of the failure on the part of a research community to be patient with failures may suffice. At one time in my life, I served on the Council of the National Institute of Allergy and Infectious Diseases. I learned a lot about how one research community operates, and I suspect the lesson applies to most research in this country. I was told that: (1) infectious hepatitis is one of the most serious, debilitating infectious diseases, and (2) practically no serious research is being conducted on it. The reason for this state of affairs was taken to be obvious by the research community. There were no really good leads for a researcher to follow. The probability was high that if he did try to conduct research, he would fail after three to five years. The research community does not reward failure, so that in all likelihood he would be fired, or at best not promoted. Hence, very few researchers want to enter this "dangerous" field. But surely this cannot be an "obvious reason" for the lack of research on infectious hepatitis. In the first place, if the research community regards excellence to be the grounds for promotion, then why can't they judge whether a failure is excellent or not, by judging the quality of the insights and ingenuities of the researcher?

Indeed, excellent failures in research may be one of the most illuminating pathways to increased understanding. To me, in a lifetime of research, failures have been the source of most of the information I have collected. I have illustrated this in Chapter 8 in Part II, which describes forty years of failure to measure human values. Here I'll give another account of the experience.

I should begin by saying that I'm not so much talking about "quantifying" human values, as I am in trying to understand them, because as the earlier chapters in their discussion of calibration have hinted, I more or less equate measurement and understanding. After all, some of the most elegant methods of classification in the history of science did not express the final results as quantities at all, although quantities often appear in the calibration process. Furthermore, there is no law, logical or legal, against assigning numbers to things, i.e., "quantifying" them. I remember attending a conference which Howard Raiffa also attended. The conference designers had announced that the topic was the quantification of risk. Howard was chairman of the final session. He told us, "Sure, we can quantify risk. It's 1.47."

I sometimes feel that my story is closely analogous to an exploration of a continent, where I have had to learn several languages and a number of dialects, and to try to understand how the inhabitants live. When Herb Simon gave the Gaither Lectures, he mentioned the fact that within the confines of the Berkeley campus, the Psychology and Economics Departments are about as far from each other as they can be. But he was referring to Behavioral Psychology, whereas my trip was to Depth Psychology, which in the main doesn't even exist on the campus.

So, I found that one day I'd be talking about utilities, the transitivity of preferences, multi-attribute values, and in such strange dialectics as cost-benefit analysis, game theory, and needs assessment. Then the next day I'd be talking about the psyche, or such archetypes as the Great Mother, Senex and Puer, and most especially about the unconscious and its values. There were also the lands of comprehensive health planning, educational evaluation, energy resources, and environmental quality. Everyone of these produced an enormous number of books and articles, each pretending to be the very latest development although many of them sounded like much the same stuff with different words. Erich Jantsch made much the same exploration, but he had a Baedecker guide which translated it all into one common language, his version of the evolution of self-organizing systems.

Finally, there were some real mysteries. Why was Tom Cowan trying to give me a twenty-year course on Joyce's *Finnegan's Wake?* What could I learn from a thirty-year course in my wife's paintings and drawings?

The story of my exploration in search of a way of measuring human values is actually a flashback to the time before the more recent discovery of my failure to understand perfection. I also failed to find the secret of the measurement of human values.

I spent my intellectual youth as a symbolic logician, so that at the beginning the behaviorists were the most attractive people to be with. Of course, there was a plethora of religious and esoteric rites of the behavioral scientists that really had very little to do with my search, so that I badly needed a sieve to separate the nonsense from the relevant. Russ Ackoff and I designed such a sieve in 1946 and called it *Psychologistics* (we had begun our work in the early 1940's, and hence the "forty years" of the exploration). Following Singer, we assumed that a person's values could be inferred from his behavior, and especially from the way in which he reacted to behavioral options. If an individual chooses action A instead of B, C, D, etc., then this may tell us something about his values, especially the value to him of future states of the world. Much like a chemist might say, there were certain impurities in any choice that need to be removed in order to get at the values themselves. If the individual is ignorant of the consequences of a choice, then his choice may not tell us anything about the value to him of a future state of the world. Also, he might simply choose the act for its own intrinsic value. Hence, we developed a calibration procedure which said in effect that to infer a value for a future state of affairs, one must do one's best to have the individual's knowledge in a good condition, and have options he doesn't value intrinsically. [20]

All this (it was a very large sieve as it turned out) seemed very satisfactory to both of us back in the 1940's and 1950's, until my restless mind began to have suspicions. These largely arose from my visits to the land of Depth Psychology and in particular to the natives who spoke Jung. You see, I had been assuming that there was an entity called an "individual" who behaved in a certain way. When I thought about the matter, I assumed that the individual was identified by his space-time pathways, much as the planets are, but that the laws of motion for humans are teleological and not physical.

But now I am in Jung's land, and the natives are all talking about the "process of individuation," but individuation certainly does not

---

20.   This calibration process, like any other, is circular, because in order, for example, to determine the state of knowledge, one has to assume values. But the circle need not be vicious.

mean space-time pathways at all. Indeed, it's very hard for a logician to understand what it means to the natives, because they've never heard of individuation in either the physical or teleological sciences.

I became fascinated by the language of these natives, because, I think, of its underlying poetry which is completely missing in the domain from which I'd come. It occurs in Jung's own writings as he discusses the heroism of the task of discovering one's self, which at the beginning is largely a mystery for most of us. If we don't know what we are as individuals, then how can our choices tell an observer anything about our "individual" values?

I can state the matter in a different way. In the domain of economics, it is usually assumed that "rational" individuals order their preferences. [21] But the question that the land of Depth Psychology raises is, "Who is talking?" Is it the Id, or Ego, or Superego in the Freudian dialect? Or in the Jungian, which archetype speaks when I say, "I prefer oranges to bananas?" If between choosing A over B, I explore my psyche a bit deeper, may I not then say I prefer B to A?

I used to believe that the natives of the land of preference orderings should be taught some depth psychology in order that they appreciate their naivete. They assume that the "I" in "I prefer A to B" is a kind of conscious ego, which it may very well be. But to depth psychology, conscious ego is only the "top" of the iceberg.

But then it occurred to me that the whole absurdity of preference orderings can easily be shown without depth psychology. There is a time of the day when I prefer whiskey to water. At the same time I often say to myself, "West, I'd prefer that you didn't prefer whiskey to water." It seems altogether reasonable that I talk to myself in this manner. At times, I get very angry with the way other drivers behave on the highway. But, when I react foolishly to their stupid maneuvers, I say to myself, "Quit that!" So, when I tell this investigator that I prefer brand A to brand B, which "I" is talking? Of course, a Freudian might tell me that this was a conversation between ego and superego. But it need not be. There have been many occasions when I've wished

---

21.   For example, if A is preferred to B, then B is not preferred to A (asymmetry). If A is preferred to B, and B to C, then A is preferred to C (transitivity).

I liked raisins, but I never felt any moral overtones in this wish. Suppose now that X says, "I prefer A to B, but I wish I didn't; and I prefer B to C, and I'm glad I do." Would you like to infer something about that person's preference for A over C without any more information?

Of course, I can hear another section of the peanut gallery screaming, e.g., those many scholars who have spent so much time on Arrow's Impossibility Theorem, the paradoxes of which arise in part from preference orderings.

In this chapter, I can't go into all my doubts about human values, doubts that began with a book I wrote in the early 1960's called *Prediction and Optimal Decision.* The book ends with a question: suppose every human being is unique. Then what can we say about his or her values? The assumption of uniqueness prevents our using class logic in our discourse, and this consequence is almost disastrous to those of us who converse almost entirely in the class logic language.

Such doubts culminated in *The Systems Approach and Its Enemies.* The "Enemies," to me, are real enough, but they don't understand values in any of the ways I'd previously encountered. They are politics, morality, religion, and aesthetics, and I've been conversing with them in this book from time to time. For example, some of the important data for planning models has to be collected through a political process. Morality generates moral outrage. The Endangered Species Act is a religious act. And aesthetics is to be a theme of the final lecture.

I'd say I've failed to understand human values, although I've learned a lot. If I were to summarize what I've learned, I'd say that there may be people who live out their conscious lives as desirers. Something creates a desire, they seek ways to satisfy it, and either do (satisfaction) or do not (frustration). Then comes another desire, and so it goes. They are the problem solvers of the first chapter. If their lives are such that they become better at satisfying their episodic desires, I'm not sure what I'd say about the design of their lives.

But all the rest, and a large "rest" it is, do not lead such lives. They may seek the process of individuation, or take on tasks like peace and nutrition, which are much too big for them. They are trouble makers, not satisficers. I don't understand them very well, but I thank God they exist.

Losing Battles. I'd now like to turn to another view of success-
failure, not of individuals alone, but in the world of social conflict, and
talk first about battles. "Battles" are not the same as "wars." A battle
is a tactical episode in a war. As every general and good chess player
knows, it may be necessary to lose a battle in order to increase one's
changes of winning the war. Chess players call this "failure" a "gambit,"
where one loses a pawn or even a piece in order to increase the chances
of winning the game.

For example, the desire of some members of the Fish and Wildlife
Service to win every battle of the Endangered Species Act often consti-
tutes a threat to the Act itself, especially when the threatened species
is so insignificant in terms of human living. After all, the Act is quite
rigid in protecting all species, and in this regard is quite unreasonable.
Even Mother Nature allows species to die. To seek to win every single
battle may be good tactics but disastrous strategy. This is why some
"friends of wildlife" fail in the long run to serve the cause of wildlife
conservation.

Sacrificing. "Sacrifice" might seem to be out of place in a chapter
on failure, until one realizes that a real sacrifice means intentionally giving up what one would otherwise regard as a high value: the failure to
continue to have a possession or a life.

Sacrifice is a basic religious design, shared by many religions around
the world. The symbol of Christian sacrifice is that God gave his only son
in order to save the souls of humanity by demonstrating his love. The Aztecs sacrificed many people by their blood in order to appease the gods
who controlled agricultural output. From the point of view of the religions that reside in us all — including atheists and agnostics — sacrifice
is terribly important and is not to be denied. Whether we worship nature;
or the oceans and mountains; or wildlife; or a god or gods, sacrifice plays
a central role.

But we humans of today who are so bound by the technological
imperative, commit a sacrilege with respect to sacrifice. We accept the
fact that in order to have the present automobile-highway system, we
must sacrifice over 50,000 human lives a year. Worse still, our develop-
ers have coined the phrase "sacrificial area" to refer to places like the
molybdenum mines of Colorado, or southern Utah-Nevada for the MX

project, that must be sacrificed to make better steel or improve our defense. The sacrifice is made to the false god called Progress, in clear violation of the First Commandment: "Thou shalt have no other gods before me."

Many of us feel we must conduct a religious war against the heretics who wish to make sacrifice the excuse for devastating the land and its living in worship of a false god.

Complete Failure. Something now needs to be said about the negative side of failure; its tragedy. To all of us, the possibility of failure becomes so excruciatingly acute that we have to experience it in imagination, as we wait to hear whether a proposed promotion has been accepted, or a job, or acquital, or whatever. Failure in our lives can be deeply tragic.

One of the best sources for dealing with tragedy is poetry. As Aristotle told us, the tragic art may be a way of cleansing the soul. My recommendation, therefore, is that one read poetic tragedy, perhaps because poetry is not analytic, does not insist on the logic of explanation (why in God's name did I fail?), but is largely elevating.

Consider, for example, Shakespeare's tragic plays. They don't analyze the failures of Lear or Hamlet; they tell us in poetic ways what failure means to the human spirit. My favorite is Richard II. In a court squabble, Richard has banished Bolingbroke and confiscated his lands. Bolingbroke has been able to convince members of the nobility to support his cause, and returns to England with enough power to threaten the King. Richard begins to realize the tragedy that he has lost the throne and expresses the loss in some of the greatest poetry of tragedy ever written:

> Let's talk of graves, of worms, and epitaphs;
> Make dust our paper, and with rainy eyes
> Write sorrow on the bosom of the earth,
>
> . . .
> . . . for within the hollow crown
> That rounds the mortal temples of a king
> Keeps Death his court; and there the antic sits,
> Scoffing his state and grinning at his pomp;
> Allowing him a breath, a little scene,
> To monarchize, be fear'd, and kill with looks;
> Infusing him with self and vain conceit,
> As if his flesh which walls about our life

Were brass impregnable; and humour'd thus,
Comes at last, and with a little pin
Bores through his castle wall, and farewell, king!
Cover your heads, and mock not flesh and blood
With solemn reverence; throw away respect,
Tradition, form and ceremonious duty;
For you have but mistook me all this while.
I live with bread, like you; feel want,
Taste grief, need friends; subjected thus,
How can you say to me, I am a king?

Note that Shakespeare does *not* say — as a psychoanalyst might — "Richard at this point realizes that abdication is a reality and resorts to various images of the killed king and his own humble humanity in order to cope with his personal uncertainty and tragedy." He says nothing of the kind, because he is a poet and the psychoanalyst is not.

Idealizing. Whoever fails must often imagine a life without failure, a heaven where all is bliss. But this largely medieval notion of heaven was severely criticized in the strenuous age of enlightenment of the seventeenth and eighteenth centuries. Chateaubriand thought the image of eternal bliss was a place of utter boredom. To live out eternal time in uninterrupted happiness was for him just another version of hell.

The same thing must be said of perfection. To be truly perfect, without any flaws, is also an unacceptable mode of the living of any life.

So, I'd like to end this excursion into the land of success and failure with some reflections about the joys of dissatisfaction. Somewhere in the *Collected Works,* Jung comments on human nature in this vein: we all say we want to avoid trouble, we all say we do our very best to keep away from it. But nonetheless we seek it out, over and over, in our lives.

As I'll be saying in chapter four, images of hell in classical religious literature are far more interesting than heaven. To many human minds, the image of hell carries us into the most acute dissatisfaction possible so that we can imagine what the ultimate dissatisfaction would be like, and this fascinates us, whereas bliss is just bliss and there's not much more one can say about it.

I don't deny that some people enjoy the idea of retirement very much, because the jobs they held were so boring, or fit their psychic needs so poorly. My next door neighbor in Bolinas thinks I should leave the University and retire to gardening, cooking, and maintenance work on my cabin there. But he gets a great kick out of fighting for the property owners of Bolinas against the awful, but powerful, Bolinas Public Utility Board. I enjoy the dissatisfactions that arise out of taking on Masters and Ph.D. students who have only a vague suspicion of an idea.

Now, episodic man, living through desire and satisfaction, is also dissatisfied in the interim periods. How do we distinguish between him and the life of wisdom I've been discussing? The answer is that in the former dissatisfaction, on occasion, ends, and that he lives to make it end. For the latter, it is endless, and he lives to keep it going. So the distinction between the two cannot be found by examining one part of life, for both live most of the time in a state of dissatisfaction. The distinction must be found in the way each designs his life.

I think I said:

(1)   Learning succeeds through failure.

(2)   Error is a kind of failure in science, but it is essential in scientific method.

(3)   Failure is often badly designed in research communities.

(4)   In my lifetime, I've failed to measure (understand) human values, and consequently learned a lot about them.

(5)   It is often essential to lose battles in order to win the war.

(6)   Sacrifice is failure for the sake of worshiping the sacred.

(7)   There is such a thing as tragic failure.

(8)   Wisdom is a life of endless inspiring dissatisfaction.

NOTE: While preparing the final draft of this chapter, I served on a Ph.D. committee for a candidate in the University of California, Berkeley, School of Education. Her completed thesis is called "Possible Relationships Among Positive Failure Feedback, Learned Helplessness and Reading Achievement in Fourth Grade," by Marguerite Dawson Boyd, 1982.

4

DESIGN OF A LIFE:
THE AESTHETICS OF CONVERSATION

In the seminars where I converse with graduate students and faculty, there inevitably grows an uneasiness, especially as we discuss such gloomy horrors as world malnutrition and the military threat. The inevitable question that the young mind creates is "what can I do about it?" I think that behind this question is the realization that the answer is *not* "stay within these safe and hallowed walls, as your professors have done." Nor is it "take a job with a multinational." In the case of malnutrition, it is more like "get thee to a village," but it is far from clear what one does when one arrives.

The question has suggested to me that I think about that very human activity that I call "designing a life." I have to admit that responding to the question "what can I do about it?" with "design your life," doesn't appear very helpful, until one realizes the pervasiveness of design in the world, and hence the many minds who can help in designing one's life. When Horst Rittel and I were serving on a committee to redesign the Design Department in the College of Environmental Design at Berkeley, we came to realize that every department on the campus has a deep concern with design: genetic design, experimental design, educational design, design of a novel, or tapestry, or musical composition, or of a management system, or design in nature. We thought of designing a Design Department to serve the campus's mutual concern for design, but politics killed our dream. Subsequently, Paul Lieber and I designed a lecture series on design in nature, design of communication systems, design in music, design of the nervous system, design in architecture, design of a life. This year we have turned our intellectual effort into a design seminar where the Chancellor, Mike Heyman, talked to us about administrative design of a university. We are now entering a third phase: a task force on designing universities.

Thought, for me, has created over the years a series of questions about design. I used to define a "system" as a set of interrelated parts with a common purpose, so that in studying systems I thought I needed first of all to understand their purposes. Then it occurred to me, probably influenced by the natives of Jung land, that the first task of all system design is people, and the number one ethical question is "who should the system serve?" For a long time, I thought that the answer to this question was "the helpless," so that, for example, the food system of the world should serve the malnourished helpless children of the ages 0-6, say. I had made "service" the central ethical foundation of planning. As the second chapter argues, among the helpless one must include future generations as well as the very young and old of our generation.

I could then see that system purpose — the goals the system should pursue — unfolded from an understanding of the plight of the helpless, whom I called the real (ethical) "clients."[22]

Gradually (I am a slow learner after all) I could see that making the concept of service a central one placed me in an awkward position. As I unfolded the people-aspect of a system, I identified two other groups besides the client. These are the decision makers, those who do or should have the power to act, i.e., change the condition of the helpless, and the planners, those who should use the human intellect to improve the human condition in thought. The decision makers have resources they can control and manipulate within an environment that matters but is out of their control. As the planner thinks about the

---

22.   This is a confusing term, and "beneficiary" may be better, because often funding agencies of government think of the agency as *the* client

decision makers, he tries to figure out how they should use their resources to serve the client best. He may do his thinking in terms of a model. Thus, a linear programming model tries to link the purposes of the system to a set of activities which the decision maker controls, subject to a set of constraints some of which are out of the decision maker's control. What is fascinating to me about linear programming models is their underlying philosophical monism. Monism is a philosophy which says that despite the diversity of the human world — in this case the diversity of goals we humans have — there is a unifying "measure of performance," appropriately symbolized in linear programming by the letter z, the last and ultimate consideration.

The measure of performance of a system, in effect weights all the system objectives, so that out of diversity springs a unity. I must confess that in my lifetime in planning, I have failed to find any plausible measures of performance of any of the systems with which I've worked. Some would like to say that the measure of performance of a university is the number of student class credit hours per dollar of cost. The faculty oppose this because we can readily see that the way to maximize such a measure of performance is to fire the faculty after their lectures have been video taped. Besides, the measure leaves out research effort.

But human curiosity often drives people to use a rather fantastic variety of measures of performance. For example, MBA programs are being constantly evaluated these days. One evaluation counted the salaries of graduates ten years later, another, the opinions of a sample of deans, yet another, the pages produced by the faculty in respectable journals.

The fact that I have failed to find a measure of performance that is above severe criticism does not mean, to me, that the concept is useless. I am a philosophical monist, and, as by this time you must have noticed, do not take failure to be the end of the story. We have learned a great deal in our efforts to discover better measures of performance. Of course, my beliefs regarding the inadequacy of measures of performance have led me into battles with those who believe in the usefulness of models in planning.

The client, decision maker, and planner could be roles played by one person, and often are, as in the case of designing one's own life. But now, I want to assume that the three groups are different, as in professional planning. Here the ethical planner has a strange and awkward role, as I've already mentioned. At one and the same time he is aware of his helpless client and the power of the decision makers who, as in the case of malnutrition, are ignoring the plight of the hungry. Even if the planner persuades the decision makers to supply food, the stability of the system is such that after a while, the food program will cease, and the hungry will be even worse off.

The planner now has the need to "intervene," i.e., to implement his plan with the guarantee that his improvement will be secure. In effect, he wants to replace the decision makers, so that he becomes what they were, with all the power they held. This is the uncomfortable position to which I alluded. Does the planner, bent on service to the ethical client, want to become a power seeker, and take over because he is ethical and "scientific"?

If one looks at the titles of books and conferences that involve planners, one is inclined to answer this question in the affirmative. Practically all the Gaither lecturers have described their interest in somehow convincing decision makers that they can do better once they accept the lecturers' advice. Three years ago, I was in Paris with some two hundred planners. Our mission, according to the conference title, was the modest one of designing a "Plan of Action for Humanity."

Because I had a growing uneasiness about the planners' role in society, I invented a fourth group in addition to clients, decision makers, and planners, which I called "system philosophers." These were people who were interested in designing the role of systems planners. They asked the very reasonable ethical question: what role should systems planners play? In the first place, they reject the idea that systems planners are "scientific" and "objective" and therefore people whose advice should automatically be followed by decision makers. Even if the systems planner has an excellent model filled with impeccable data, it does not follow that the decision makers of the world should adopt the model's conclusions about the correct course of action. For one thing, the decision makers are political and therefore realistic, whereas the model is based on some version of rationality. It would be wrong to say that the decision makers are "irrational." They are neither rational nor irrational, because they operate in the political world of "neither of the above."

As far as I am aware, none of my Gaither colleagues was a systems philosopher, because none of them discussed his role in the affairs that concerned him or her. This is not intended to be a criticism of my predecessors. Neither Fred Balderston nor I in our invitations asked them to be self-reflective, i.e., philosophical. We did expect them to be thoughtful, but not necessarily lovers of wisdom.

System philosophers, in other words, want to spend some of their lives on the design of their life, and, through thought, generalize from such considerations to the design of any life, whether of a planner or any other career or mode of living.

Thus far, I have let thought say some things about design, that design must consider the clients and their purposes and measure of performance, the decision makers and their resources and environment, the planners and implementation and guarantors of securing improvement. Then I introduced the system philosophers and one of their "enemies," politics. Now I need to say something about "life."

Three currents of thought seem to have come together as I pondered the meaning of life in the phrase "design of a life." One was a strange experiment some of us conducted in the 1950's at Case Institute of Technology. The National Science Foundation was interested in communication between scientists, and most especially in the importance of reading articles, reports, and books. We chose a sample of researchers in biology and chemistry and equipped them with wristwatches with alarms that went off at random during the waking day. When the alarm went off, the researcher was to note on a card he carried just what he was doing at the time. (We provided him with a class of activities, including "other" to take care of possible embarrassments.) Much to some people's surprise, the scientists only spent 6% of their time reading anything, including newspapers. On the other hand, they spent well over half their time in conversations with their colleagues.

The second hint came from my experience in psychoanalysis in the 1960's. I came to realize that the whole of the analysis was a very long conversation both with myself and with my analyst. Somehow, I was to learn about myself and the process of individuation through conversation.

The third hint came from a long-time inter st in the meaning of consciousness. Strangely enough, although psychoanalysts spend a great deal of time on the unconscious, they have remarkably little to say about the conscious mind, possibly because many of them think they and we know it "directly." The unconscious is supposed to be deep and dark, like the bottom of the ocean, and the conscious is light and above water. In the San Francisco Bay Area there are hundreds of workshops on "raising consciousness," as though consciousness were much like a sunken ship, or perhaps a loaf of bread.

Singer tried his hand at defining consciousness. He did so by examining its historical roots. The "con" means "with" and the "sciousness" comes from "scio," "to know." Hence consciousness is a "knowing with," i.e., the phenomenon of an observer observing an observer.

This is all very helpful to me, but my three streams of reflection were telling me that consciousness may be characterized as conversation. That idea sent me to the Oxford Dictionary. There, I found two obsolete definitions of conversation:

(1)   The action of living or having one's being *in* a place or *among* people.

(2)   The action of having dealings with others; living together.

So conversation does not mean just talk, but is far more general.

I don't think that saying consciousness is conversation really defines consciousness. It's more helpful than saying, as do some psychologists, that "consciousness is awareness either of oneself or of other entities." But I see no way of defining consciousness in the same manner in which we define things like the brain or heart. The reason is that consciousness is not a concept, but resides in the domain of the aesthetic.

"Aesthetics" is a word about which there has been some considerable debate among philosophers. Its origins among the Greeks indicate that it was closely connected with sense perception. Later on, its meaning changed considerably when the German eighteenth century philosopher, Baumgarten, called it "criticism of taste." Kant, in his *Critique of Pure Reason,* in the section on the Transcendental Aesthetic, reverted to the original Greek meaning, namely, the forms of sensation. Baumgarten won out in philosophy departments, where courses in aesthetics deal with such matters as the meaning of great art. The courses themselves tend to be quite unaesthetic, i.e., dull and unenlightening.

I have come to use the term "aesthetics" in a sense that is neither

of the above. I think there is a quality in both conversation and consciousness that can be described as "radiant," or "lively," and that this
quality defies conceptual defining. I'm not denying that the experience
of art has the aesthetic quality, but such experience by no means ex-
hausts all the ways the aesthetic appears to us.

To summarize thus far. I'm interested in the design of a life, by
which I mean the design of an aesthetic conversation. One response to
those who want to know "what can I do about it," is to say "design
your life as an aesthetic conversation."

Now I can return to the awkward position of the planner. As long
as planners perceived themselves as serving the helpless, they could not
avoid taking on the superior position. If you are helpless, and I come
along and give you help, then I serve you and you don't serve me. You
converse with me since you by your condition tell me how helpless you
are. I converse with you in a way totally different from yours, because
I try to provide help. Hence, our conversation is not a "living together."
You live one way, I another. Our conversation lacks the aesthetic.
Hence, it was my emphasis on service that created the awkward role
for the planner.

Some of my friends say they are trying to promote humanistic
medicine, by which they mean, in my language, that they would like
to change the relationship between the doctor and patient from service
to conversation. This doesn't mean that the doctor gives up his role
as medical expert, but it does mean that the doctor respects the unique
expertise of the patient. Some of us struggle to accomplish the same
thing in education, because every student has a knowledge that no
teacher possesses. As for malnutrition, every village dweller has a knowledge about village life that no researcher can acquire from his visits,
interviews and statistics.

All this amounts to a speculation about the design of the life of
a planner. The planner can, of course, design his planning life to be a
life devoted to helping the helpless and bear the confusion of being both
a helper and a superior. But there is another design of a planner's life,
one in which he cooperates in designing a "level" conversation with the
clients. The planner has an understanding the client lacks, but also the
client has an understanding the planner lacks. Both have "needs." The
planner needs to help, the client needs to be helped. Of course, the

unaesthetic utilitarian will butt in on this idyllic scene and point out that the planner also needs to be paid in order to make a living by his level conversation, and his demand for salary is based on his superiority.

In any event, I think I've said enough for the time being about the design of the life of a philosophical planner, and I'd like to change the topic of the conversation by exploring some of the themes of conversation. To begin, I'll go back to the first lecture. There, I was arguing the need for ethics in managing and planning. Now I can say more about this need, because ethics is no more nor less than an aesthetic conversation on such topics as equity, happiness, responsibility, and so on. Thought sometimes wants ethics to stop and reach conclusions in the form of moral or legal codes, which usually turn out to be quite unaesthetic, but wisdom realizes that ethics is an eternal conversation. One of its joys is a conversation with our ancestors. I find textbooks on ethics to be incredibly boring and uninspiring. The conversation becomes much more radiant if you read the original, e.g., in a good translation. When I was a graduate student, my scholarly professors criticized Jowett's translation of Plato's dialogues because of his sloppy scholarship, but in his hands the conversations of the dialogues take on a life of their own.

The reason that ethical relativism ("different strokes for different folks") is so bad is that it stops the conversation. One of my colleagues in the Business School became quite angry when the subject of ethics arose in a Ph.D. oral examination. "All matters of ethics are relative," he shouted, "there are no absolute values!" All I could think to say was "are you sure?" Relativists are only sure of one thing, their relativism. They actually think that ethics is the search for absolute values, and since it is, it is a hopeless enterprise. Since ethics is an eternal conversation, its conversation retains its aesthetic quality if human values are regarded as neither relative nor absolute.

I mentioned the fact that in our human world there are conversation killers — or perhaps "murderers" is a better term since they kill off a life. These murderers have many weapons besides relativism and its "it all depends." They say "that's about the stupidest remark I ever heard," or "what nonsense," or "he doesn't have the vaguest idea of what economic theory means." The conversation murderers are plentiful in academic society. They often infiltrate Ph.D. oral examinations; once you murder the conversation of an oral, the candidate is done for.

But there are far more serious conversation killers in our society. Recently I've begun to learn a bit about the psychology of the disabled, inspired, I think, by the courageous life of Ed Roberts, director of the Department of Rehabilitation in Sacramento, California. Ed had a serious case of polio when he was fourteen; the result was almost total paralysis from the neck down. His parents were told by some medical "experts" that he would have to spend the rest of his life "as a vegetable," a phrase that means (to me) that all conversation other than what takes place between ourselves and inedible vegetables would have to cease. Ed's mother decided this was nonsense, and she and Ed began designing a life for him, a life of getting degrees, teaching, and now administration in the state government, even though he must spend a significant part of the day in an iron lung and a wheelchair. I've learned that the psychology of rehabilitation is designing attitudes not only of the disabled with respect to their lives, but also of the public with respect to their conversations with the disabled. Ed's case is unusual; a very large majority of seriously disabled people are cut off from conversations with their fellow countrymen.

Similar remarks could be made about convicted criminals and the convicted elderly, both of whom we treat in remarkably similar ways. The idea seems to be that if you are convicted of having committed a crime or of being seriously old, you should be isolated from the rest of the world, all conversations being eliminated except with a few like you. What an unaesthetic design of ethics our society has created!

Part of the conversation of ethics is action, when we let our acts and their consequences converse with us on matters of morality. Our active lives are an integral part of our lifetime of ethical conversation. Some things grow in such a life: for me equity — never treating others or myself as means only — seems to have grown a lot as I realized the aesthetic quality of equity.

So at this point I need to reiterate a theme of the second chapter, namely, that so-called "action" is really not very different in its quality from deliberation. Implementation problems begin to disappear when we understand that so-called action does not change the topic of the conversation completely. Passing the Endangered Species Act was, in effect, just another piece of the conversation among all of us about wildlife and with wildlife.

In the second chapter I tried my hand at designing a conversation with future generations. The Endangered Species Act and the preservation of wilderness areas are aspects of such a conversation. Thought has some trouble imagining a conversation with people who will live 25,000 years from now, a time span over which some of our generation's wastes will continue to pollute. But such pollution is in fact our design of a very unaesthetic conversation with them. So is the claim that some future generation will be smart enough to discover what should be done with the waste.

The third chapter was a conversation with failure. I should note that conversation need not be confined to people alone. When I conducted experiments in physical chemistry during World War II, I felt that I was in a real conversation with Nature; the design of the conversation was called experimental design. Earlier, when I began proving theorems in symbolic model logic, there was a most exciting conversation with the symbols on a page. Hence, I think that it may be helpful if people in their lives designed conversations with their failures.

Thought would like to ask about unaesthetic conversations. These have the quality I mentioned earlier, of non-symmetry of respect between the participants: murder, rape, exploitation (slavery, starvation, oppression), routine jobs, and authoritarianism.

I'd like to add one more topic of conversation about conversation. A few weeks ago I gave a lecture on the design of conversational lives, and afterwards I was driving alongside of the beautiful Bolinas Lagoon in California. Spinoza came and sat in the other front seat, with the ease the spirits of our ancestors seem to acquire. He reminded me that in his *Improvement of the Understanding* he had designed a hierarchy of the designs of education. The lowest, he said, was *hearsay,* where the teacher tells the students about various facts, and they write them down, and later, using memory, spill them out in their examination books. The next level is *by rule,* as in carpentry and cooking, where the young carpenter learns that a roof that is three feet high and goes out four feet, will be five feet wide (5-4-3 rule), or the apprentice cook that he should add one teaspoon of salt per one quart of water in boiling noodles. The third level is *by principles,* as in engineering or geometry, where the student learns the basic postulates and the method of deducing the rules from them (so that the 5-4-3 rule follows from

$a^2 + b^2 = c^2$ in a right triangle, and this theorem follows from the postulates of geometry). Finally, the highest level is *intuition*, which grasps the truth of the postulates directly. Spinoza's question was whether any or all of this was useful in thinking about the design of conversations.

So we conversed a bit, and came up with the following conversational designs, but not necessarily a hierarchy of designs:

(1)   Perhaps the nearest analogy to hearsay, is the conversation about the doings of friends, enemies, big shots, etc., commonly known as "gossip," but not in the negative sense alone.

(2)   The analogy of "by rule" is "trivia," a word used in Roman times when travelers met where three roads came together. ("Hi, Joe, long time no see; how's the wife and kids?" "Fine, how's yours." "Fine." "Whaty'a been doing?")

(3)   The analogy of learning principles all agree upon, is the conversation of agreement, or what might be called reinforcing conversations, where the participants agree on the answer to some issue. ("Isn't the administration's policy on inflation absurd?" "It sure is; just like most of their policies." "How could they ever think that . . .?")

(4)   Intuitive conversations might be called the conversations of curiosity, where the participants don't necessarily agree, but are truly anxious to find what the other is saying and why. ("That's terribly interesting. I wouldn't have thought of putting it that way. Can you explain a little more what you mean by so-and-so?") The word curiosity comes from the same root as "careful," so that the curious carefully explore the other's ideas without damaging them.

Naturally, there are other conversations, e.g., fights and games, where the conversationalists oppose each other, or the dance, where they support each other. Indeed, one of the aesthetic delights of human conversations is the invention of new kinds, e.g., new kinds by lovers.

One more comment. The rational planner is a participant in the conversation about the ways of changing the human condition. He (she) is neither right nor wrong. He must contribute to the conversation, as must politics, morality, and religion. In *The Systems Approach and Its Enemies,* I said that the rational planner must "be" his enemies. Now I can say it more to my own taste: He must learn to design aesthetic conversations with them. So after I finished *The Systems Approach and Its Enemies,* I set to work designing such aesthetic conversations about matters that concern my planning mind. I had five characters in what I, perhaps unaesthetically, called conversational analysis. They were: deterministic systems approaches, teleological systems approaches, politics, morality, and religion. On the subject of world malnutrition, they said things like the following:

Deterministic systems approach: malnutrition is an inevitable aspect of the evolution of the human spirit — a bifurcation of humanity into the poor and wealthy — that will pass as the evolutionary self-organization principles express themselves.

Teleological systems approach: we should be able to do something about it, because it is a matter of changing the distribution system of food and not just the production system. India now has a surplus of grain. We need to learn how to redesign its distribution system, using political power as our means.

Politics talks about greed and power — the realities of human nations.

Morality talks about moral outrage and the need for a material revolution.

Religion talks about a truly human universal religious upheavel that will unite all of humanity in a spiritual revolution.

I've found that the design of such conversations has been very helpful to me in learning about an area of concern, much more helpful than the dialetical conversations I designed earlier which turned out to be too rational. [23]

Before ending, I'd like to read you a dialogue I wrote for Thought and Wisdom.

A DIALOGUE BETWEEN THOUGHT AND WISDOM ON DEATH

Thought: I have been listening to our conversation on the design of a life and reading E.A. Singer's similar discussion in his *Search of a Way of Life,* where he tries to put together the design based on desire fulfillment and design based on ideal seeking. His last chapter has to

---

21.   C. West Churchman, *The Design of Inquiring Systems* (NY: Basic Books, 1971), Ch. 7, Hegelian Inquiring Systems.

face what thought cannot possibly deny, namely, the end of life and
what lies beyond. Thought cannot deny that there is a "beyond," because of the way we humans think about time. We haven't always
thought about it in the same way; Kant more or less shattered Hume's
thinking on the subject, and perhaps the new physics-chemistry of Illya
Prigogine and his colleagues will shatter some classical notions. But
none of this changes the macro-image that there is a real beyond for
all our lives; an end-of-life and a beyond. Thought over the ages has
created many maps of the beyond. A blank map with nothing whatever sketched upon it. A soul which exists in some state; heavenly,
hellish, limbo-like. A reincarnation into another life. I wonder what
you, Wisdom, have to say on this matter?

Wisdom: It's a curious matter. As you know, you, Thought,
cannot thrive without evidence. It's really your basis of conversation.
You build your mansions out of it, you seek to mine it through your
experiments and deductive processes. I could see you frown deeply
when I introduced Hope into the conversation. What did you do?
You immediately thought that if Hope could be so cheerfully accepted
in the discourse, why not invite Despair as well? It's only fair, after
all, and you take fairness to be absolutely essential in all conversations.
I don't, because fairness is about equality and not about the real moral
issue, equity.

But there is no evidence at all about the beyond. Not evidence
in your sense, at least. Part of the reason is that there is remarkably little
of what you call evidence about the before-the-beyond. In the age of
dissent of the 1960's, some wag designed a sign that asked, "Is there
life after birth?" We can say that there is consciousness and consciousness is conversation, but none of that is real evidence that conscious
life exists. Some thoughtful people like Ross Ashby conceive of life
as the workings of a machine-like, cybernetic brain, but he never
generated any evidence that machines, no matter how complex, have
a consciousness like ours.

Since evidence about life-and-death is lacking, you, Thought, have
two choices. One is quite matter-of-fact, and is the one chosen by
Singer. As he discusses Kant's condition of the immortality of the
Good Will, he tells us that Kant could find no evidence of such

immortality. Nor, for him, can "science," which was Singer's name for you. But there is evidence that not only will there be a beyond, but also there will be people in it — future generations. And, for Singer, you can design your life so that their lives will be "stronger" — his word for "nearer to the ideal." You will live in them and, as you your-self admit, the conversation between yourself and them may well con-tinue. But this idea of immortality may not please you.

Your second choice is to elevate a function you often use but never believe without evidence. It is imagination. It is quite common to regard mathematics to be the science of pure thought, until one rea-lizes the strong role that imagination has played in the history of that science. All the great conjectures come out of superb imaginings, some of them eventually proved by the evidence of deduction, some not.

Now if on the subject of the beyond you could let imagination have its say, completely without evidence, what a joy you might have! Or, a joy, mixed with some tingling horrors. As I mentioned earlier, hell is a lot more interesting to imagination than heaven. Consider this example:

> This morning we endeavored, in our reflection upon hell, to imagine the material character of that awful place.
>
> Hell is a strait and dark and foul smelling prison, an abode of demons and lost souls, filled with fire and smoke . . .
>
> In earthly prisons the poor captive has at least some liberty of movement . . . Not so in hell. There, by reason of the great number of the damned, the pris-oners are heaped together in their awful prison, the walls of which are said to be four thousand miles thick: and the damned are so utterly bound and helpless that . . . they are not even able to remove from the eye a worm that gnaws it. [24]

Once when I was giving a class to seniors in high school, I invited them to imagine the beyond and their imagination produced some mar-velous results. My own went back to the idea of decision, and to all the life-designs that had been cut off by our constantly snipping off the

---

24.   James Joyce, *A Portrait of an Artist as a Young Man.*

branches of possible life designs. The beyond is to be spent, in eternity, in exploring these branches, each of which is constantly creating new branches.

So you see, my dear Thought, how you deprive yourself by insisting that Imagination has to go along with Evidence. If you could only give up this idea, you could really have a great time with the beyond; drawing it, painting it, writing poems and narratives about it, enriching your life and the lives of others.

Thought: That leaves me thoroughly dissatisfied. There is a third option. After all my struggles, the basic reality of Nature still remains a mystery. To me, it makes a lot of sense to say that once we begin to understand how living beings are related to the nonliving, we will begin also to understand the beyond. Until then, speculation and conjectures are appropriate, but they must be tied to our understanding of evidence that the future may create.

Wisdom: But of course you don't surprise me, dear Thought. You're just where I always expect you to be in your restless life: in a state of hopeful dissatisfaction!

PART II

5

WILLINGNESS TO PAY AND MORALITY:
A STUDY OF FUTURE VALUES

In my mind's eye I can imagine a young hunter watching a beautiful herd of buffalo from a convenient height amid the plains of mid-19th century America. I can also imagine a young lover of nature looking over the same view a century later. Now with the facility of imagination I can bring the two together. What conversation might take place? What would progeny say to progenitor about the contrasting scenes? Would progeny blame progenitor for the buffalo slaughter, remind him of his thoughtless neglect, or simply forgive and forget and accept the plains as they are today?

In all my adventures into values — ethical and moral — I have rarely encountered any deep discussion of the values our progeny will hold most dear, or what these values should mean to us. I think that one cause of this amazing negligence is that we don't know how to reason on such a topic. Reason, we have discovered, is not a function which operates in a vacuum, creating its own materials and deducing great truths from them. Reason, rather, requires some considerable degree of knowledge to accomplish its task. And apparently we have little secure knowledge about the values of our progeny. Of course, on a very superficial level we can assume that they will not want to starve, or otherwise die in a miserable environment. But what elevating or glorious values will dominate their lives? Will the sight of a large flock of whooping cranes bring enduring joy to so many? What reasoned steps would lead us to a conclusion one way or the other?

There is another reason, besides a lack of knowledge, why our concern for future values is so difficult for us to discuss objectively: these are our children, we their parents. Parents are rarely even sensitive about their children's values, because deep, archetypal feelings get in the way in the form of anxiety, or horror, or moral joy or indignation.

Nevertheless, I intend here to try to say something reasonable about future values. To do so, I'll begin by being ridiculous, with the comforting thought that any step away from this initial position must be "more" rational, i.e., have a modicum of rationality in it.

The ridiculous conversation between progenitor-hunter H and progeny-nature lover N goes as follows:

H: I can realize that you feel hurt because my hunter instincts virtually obliterated the buffalo from the scene of the plains. But you must realize that I, like you, am human and I desperately wanted to hunt down the buffalo — not only for the profit but for the joy of the kill.

N: I think what makes me saddest of all is that my children, and their children, will never see this world as you saw it. Your desire wiped out the joys of countless generations.

H: I've been thinking about that, and appreciate your point. But I've come up with a rational plan which should take care of this matter of endless value-losses. Suppose we could estimate what each nature lover would be willing to pay to see such a buffalo-laden scene in any given period of time. Then my generation should create a trust fund to pay such frustrated progeny for the lost opportunity caused by our slaughtering the buffalo. The trust fund, of course, would be bolstered by interest over the years, and managed so as to minimize the fluctuations in the money market. Thus, you see, we should ask ourselves the straightforward economic question: Are we willing to pay the amount required by the trust fund for the pleasures of slaughtering the buffalo? If so, then I cannot see that my progeny can blame me; to them I bequeath the trust fund to be used for alternative sources of pleasure. I note in passing that the trust fund need not be infinite, or even very large, since interest rate and GNP will keep increasing its value and there may be comparatively few nature lovers in any given generation. On the other hand, the required trust fund might be a strong deterrent against our harming wildlife if the required amount were too large. In other words, in our wildlife planning we'd have to subtract the size of the trust fund from *our* willingness to pay, and if the result is negative, we keep our hands off. Of course, the "trust fund" may not actually exist; it is a concept to be used in deciding about wildlife policies.

N: (He is trying his best to be decently respectful to his forefather.) But look here, I don't *want* you to pay me (bribe me?) so that you can kill buffalo. Suppose you'd had this same urgent desire to kill off all the women of your time; *then* what should you pay me who wouldn't exist.

H: But that's absurd! But of course we should not adopt a policy which eliminates all our progeny. But I call to your attention that some economists of your time have proposed an idea similar to mine with respect to controlling human population, namely, that each adult-pair be assigned 22 deciles of human babies which they can sell or buy on the open market. It's the same "willingness to pay" concept.

N: (calming down, but still indignant) Since you're using an economist of my age, why don't I bring in as witness a philosopher of yours? Kant enunciated the moral principle that we make our own policy choices on the basis that the principle underlying the policy can be made a universal law, applicable to all under all circumstances. His moral principle is the concept of moral fairness extended to its ultimate. The application of your "willingness to pay" idea is the following: Whenever any generation is willing to pay its progeny for the destruction of any aspect of Nature, it has the moral right to do so. We've already seen that the generalization does not hold for people; not even for classes of people, I hope. Some of your generation seems to have been willing to destroy blacks and yellows, some of mine to destroy the Jewish race. I don't suppose that either you or I as reasonable men could ever condone such practice on moral grounds no matter what trust fund was created. Nor does it make much sense to ask whether I am willing to pay to see all the progeny of a pregnant black woman who died in the hold of a slave ship.

Now, dear ancestor, I come back to the buffalo, and ask what is it about buffalo which makes the willingness-to-pay principle valid when the principle fails so miserably for people?

H: O.K., but I'm not ready at all to abandon my principle, even in the face of Kant's moral law. You have merely given examples of bad management, not bad morals. My generation often paid very little for starving people, and yours is much the same in this respect. But both yours and mine eventually paid — in revolutions, civil wars, assassinations and so on. Were either of us better managers, we would pay the price we were eventually forced to pay, and instead have chosen policies which did not sacrifice people's lives. But note that in wars and in transportation both our generations have been willing to pay the price of destroying lives.

N: You've wandered from your first formulation into another version of your principle, in which, in effect, you put all relevant generations together into one large system, with the principle that we ought to maximize the total net benefit across all generations. But now your reasoning gets hopelessly tangled, because "benefit" is to be measured in terms of "willingness to pay," but the "willingness to pay" has to be assessed in terms of the total system benefits. At the outset, you painted yourself as the eager young hunter who was willing to pay me so many dollars for the thrill of killing the buffalo. Now you paint yourself as the wise planner, whose willingness to pay comes from large-scale prudential considerations: the lust to kill has been replaced by calm reflection.

At this point in the discussion, the old Hunter, weary of the questioning and relentless logic, no doubt evoked the words of one of his contemporaries and turned on the young nature lover with:

"I have answered three questions, and this is enough,"
Said his father, "Don't give yourself airs!
Do you think I can listen all day to such stuff?
Be off, or I'll kick you downstairs!"

But we, in a more sober mood, can summarize the three questions: (1) is there an appropriate "willingness to pay" principle based on one generation's judgment about what future generations should receive as payment for present generation deprivations which can be applied to forming policy decisions about the preservation or nonpreservation of a wildlife species? (2) or, should such a principle be justified on moral grounds, e.g., by the use of Kant's moral law? (3) or, can the principle be justified on "systems" grounds, e.g., by showing that, properly applied, it best serves the values of all relevant generations?

I'm inclined to say that our reasoning powers are not at present adequate to respond to these questions well enough because our knowledge base is still too weak. But I don't think the discussion should stop at this point, because I believe we have another common resource to aid our judgment making, namely, our common feelings. These are not easy to formulate precisely, sometimes seem to change unpredictably, but exist nonetheless and have a great deal to do with the quality of our lives.

The first suggestion, that a generation "pay" its progeny for removing the opportunity to observe a wildlife species is the ridiculous beginning to which I eluded earlier. It's not merely ridiculous from a rational thinking point of view (how in the world would a progenitor ever determine such prices?), but it also ridiculously inappropriate from the feeling side. The whole imaginary transaction of one person handing money to another so that the hunter can destroy as he pleases is simply a horror picture. This ridiculous suggestion is "better" than doing nothing at all, as say our progenitors did with respect to the buffalo; *they* apparently didn't even have the common decency to think of their progeny at all, or even to tell us they were sorry.

In order to improve on the first suggestion, the lover of nature suggested that we evoke Kant's moral law, that the principle underlying a policy of preservation or destruction be framed as a rational universal; otherwise, the policy must be considered immoral. But now the opposite of the first suggestion seems to occur. In the first suggestion a callous generation could easily decide to pay damned little to its progeny for destroying a species; under Kant's moral law, it looks as though very few generations if any would ever be justified in meddling with the life-style of *any* species. The point is made when the progeny naturelover asks his elder what it is about buffalos which makes the willingness-to-pay principle valid, when the principle fails for people. Across the ages, our progenitors have often replied "there is nothing," and also "there is everything." The answer "these is nothing" extends Kant's moral law to all mammals, at least. The answer "there is everything" limits the law to mankind (or even, for some, to an elite of mankind).

There is something deeply embarrassing about the second reply; it sends philosophers scurrying off to find that quality which not only distinguishes humans from other species but makes them vastly superior — infinitely superior, really. The philosophers have replied variously: we can reason, contemplate, laugh, write our history, cry, mourn our dead, kill ourselves more effectively, pollute better, and so on. The joke on ourselves is sardonic: we are the only species which asks what makes itself unique.

I think our wisdom and perspective about wildlife requires that we explore in great depth the less embarrassing reply; there is nothing except expediency which differentiates the buffalo and ourselves. We are expedient creatures and therefore from time to time we will do something expedient — slaughter buffalos, kill all the fish in a lake, wipe out a species of bird by altering its natural habitat — and when we do we must recognize that what we do is immoral.

I realize how harsh this last remark must sound to many innocents. But it is really astonishing how often we resist admitting our immorality as social beings, while being quite willing to accept our inefficiency as social managers.

Kant gave us a gem of reasoning in this regard. He appreciated that social humans must obey what he called the "prudential" imperative — what we today recognize as the basis of our reasoned socioeconomic policies. These policies are supposed to serve the "whole" relevant system, though even today we don't know what this means in any precise sense. But Kant also recognized that an excellent prudential imperative would in all likelihood require treating some people as means only, and not as ends (some will be drafted, some will work at jobs they hate, some will be economically deprived). Hence, says Kant any "good" social policy (prudential imperative) will be likely (certain?) to be immoral in some regard. "Progress", for Kant, is the convergence of a prudential world and a moral world.

If we borrow this idea from Kant, then we recognize that both the second and the third answers above are necessary aspects of a rational approach to future values, e.g., concerning wildlife policy. We must surely do our best to apply the systems approach to wildlife, and estimate the socio-economic benefits and costs of any policy across all relevant generations. But we should also apply our moral judgments to proposed policies. If we deem it expedient to put a paper mill on a stream in the Ozarks because thereby we can provide employment to the impoverished, we should also declare to ourselves that the policy, while expedient, is also immoral because it destroys fish and wildlife. There is no need to feel ashamed if such clauses are added, though a bit of humility may be in order.

What I am suggesting is that a "moral assessment" be added to the evaluation of national programs like sport fish and wildlife. For this suggestion to be sound I should say more about what would be entailed in making such judgments. To do so, I'll return to the conversation between progenitor and progeny once more, because there the basis of moral judgment was left up in the air.

We said that a policy, such as the permission to slaughter buffalo, was to be judged moral or immoral depending on whether the principle underlying the policy could be made a universal law of nature. If we accept the ridiculousness of any "willingness to pay" principle, especially as applied to nonhumans, then what shall replace it? Why, I think a most obvious principle that *does* have a universal flavor to it, namely, that the principle we should apply to our relationship to other living species is above all natural: we should relate to them as species naturally relate to each other. Of course, I should hasten to point out that I don't know what I'm talking above — very well. As a layman I know that bees relate to plants in mutually helpful ways, that spiders relate to flies with less mutual assistance, and so on.

It helps somewhat if I come back to hunting and fishing. At first blush, the hunter appears to treat the hunted as means only, so that all hunting apparently must be deemed immoral, if Kant's moral law is valid. But this is absurd; among the absurdities is that all spiders, bears, all fish of the sea, are all immoral. The absurdity disappears once we realize the principle that underlies hunting among the natural species: it is the preservation of a natural relationship which sustains the order of nature. Nature as an organic whole works in part through the hunter-hunted principle. To hunt where the principle of hunting is to sustain the natural order is not immoral, because the principle is a universal law of nature.

Our trouble as humans is that our reflective intelligence and imagination get in our way in trying to appreciate ourselves as a species. We can easily imagine that the spider gloats over his helpless kill, and make immoral monsters of them all. We also go to the opposite extreme and declare that we should preserve all species (or at least all non-insect species). Is this part of our natural role as a species? Why should it be?

The conclusion seems to be this: *to understand our moral obligation in making wildlife policy is just the same as to understand humans as a natural species.* And our obligation to our progeny is that we never commit acts which will deprive them of having a natural relationship to any other species. The immorality of the buffalo scene lay in its general slaughter. It may also have lain in the fact that it is unnatural for humans to hunt buffalo, though that would be a far more difficult matter to establish. I don't think it's going to be an easy matter to understand ourselves as a natural species, but I also think that we can already entertain some basis for moral assessment of wildlife programs.

6

A SENSE OF LIFE:
PERSPECTIVES OF WILDLIFE POLICIES
REGARDING ENDANGERED SPECIES

". . . every one members one of another."   Romans 12

Introduction

The past quarter century has witnessed an intense interest in evaluating human projects, and especially those supported by taxpayer's money. Since money has been the source of the project, it is only reasonable to expect that money should be the basis of evaluation: one can best justify the expenditure of his money to a taxpayer if one can show that the return (to him?) is three-fold or ten-fold. This reasonable expectation has led to the various techniques of cost-benefit analysis, most of which tend to be rather crude and unsatisfactory, but nonetheless perhaps the best we have.

However, it is important to note that some of our governmental projects have incredibly long-term implications. The threats of nuclear waste may last as long as 300,000 years, and the lowering of a water table in the desert may not be reversible for 25,000 years. To these long-term projects belongs the preservation of wildlife. If human intervention brings the end of a species, then the "long-term impact" may be forever; "may be," because technology knows no technical impossibilities.

73

But given our present state of knowledge, we are not justified in assuming that some brilliant genetic engineer of the future will find the way to recreate lost species.

By law, the taxpayer does pay his money in the USA to preserve endangered species. How can we justify his payments? What "reimbursement" does he receive for what he has payed? One answer — not a very good one — is that he and his neighbor enjoy seeing a whooping crane or an esoteric bug, and that in general one should pay for what one enjoys. Just how to estimate the dollar value of such enjoyment is not clear, but perhaps no more difficult than the dollar value of any enriching hour of recreation.

The reason the answer is not a good one is that there is a vast population of people who may sometime enjoy the spectacle of a whooping crane — all future generations, in fact. Since their enjoyments are spread over the indefinite future, even if we assign a small amount to each hour, the total dollar value of enjoyment grows indefinitely.

We might then conclude that we had found the economic justification of the endangered species act: its economic value is indefinitely large. However, this conclusion comes much too soon. For one thing, the costs each generation incurs to sustain the few hours of enjoyment may far exceed the benefits. But even if the benefits exceed the costs, today's taxpayer has a right to ask why he should pay for the enjoyments of future generations. I've heard several planners raise the question, "What have future generations done for me?"

I know of no better reply to this rather crass question than good old-fashioned moral equity, which says that we humans share our lives together, together with all those who live when we do, as well as those who have lived and will live. This rather common sense political philosophy can be debated, of course, but I'm not inclined to do so here; an egoistic skeptic is invited to reflect on where he might be today if his ancestors had considered his well being to be largely irrelevant with respect to their goals.

Therefore, we must include the joys and sorrows of future generations in our economic calculations of the value of the Fish and Wildlife Service project to preserve the species. Have we not found our sought-for-justification, as long as the benefits for each coming generation exceed the costs?

The answer is "no", because we have ignored a central piece of logic of cost-benefit analysis, namely, that a future benefit is worth less than a present benefit. A simple argument for this axiom is that if I present an opportunity for a joyful event today, as opposed to an equally joyful event tomorrow, you'd better choose today because tomorrow you may be dead. A more refined argument is that if I give you a choice between $100 today and $100 a year from now, you'd be wise to select the former because (at the least) you can invest today's $100 in a savings account and a year from now you'd have, say, $106 at 6 percent interest. Economists call this hidden value of the present the "discount rate". Thus if the savings account is the best you can do with the present $100, then the discount rate is 6 percent. Evidently, after a while, a future return compared to a present return vanishes toward zero: $100 today is worth a lot more, according to the axiom, than $2,000 a century from now at a 6 percent discount rate per annum.

However, the discount axiom apparently runs into difficulties as applied to future generations, because the recipient of the return is different from the present-day taxpayer. Neither "I may be dead tomorrow" nor "I will have $106 a year from now" seems to apply. If the moral postulate of equity holds, then the enjoyment of a person in a future generation — no matter how distant — is at least as valuable as my present enjoyment.

In Chapter 5, I tried to show how this apparent paradox might be solved. The idea is that money invested grows just as future generations' enjoyment grows. Hence, if today we who are living decide we want to eliminate the egret to make fancy hats for the Easter parade, we would set aside a "trust fund" to pay every future person who might have enjoyed the egret for his loss of enjoyment. Thus, we would attempt to estimate how many hours of egret-viewing enjoyment would occur in the year 2006, if egrets were still alive, multiply by the dollar value of such enjoyment (in 1976 dollars, say), subtract the cost of maintaining the species, and arrive at a 2026 "benefit minus cost" estimate. Then we would calculate the size of a trust fund which, in principle, could pay the 2026 citizens for our having destroyed the egret. Since the trust fund makes money by its investments, it need not be infinitely large; it need only be large enough to take care of the "enjoyment demands" of each generation.

Of course, there would be serious difficulties in making the required estimates (there might be a fad of egret viewers in 2026, or all long-legged birds might be an anathema), but the technical difficulties do not appear much worse than those facing most cost-benefit analysis.

(Of course, the trust fund need not actually be established; it is only to be used to compute the cost of a policy which permits the destruction of a species.)

My earlier account depicted a later-generation nature lover shouting at his ancestor — a buffalo killer — that he did not want to be paid for not seeing a buffalo, that such payment by no means alleviated his moral indignation at wanton killing of another species. I took his indignation seriously, and attempted to develop another way of evaluating long-term policies based on the moral precept that every species should behave "naturally" with respect to other species. In this chapter, I plan to explore this idea in greater depth.

A Logical Interlude: Can We Avoid Teleology?

There seems to be little doubt that people who are strongly developed in the feeling function are repelled by the proposal that one generation pay another for its moral depravity in slaughtering a species. But the "thinking types" apparently have an unanswerable argument for their case. This can be illustrated within the human species itself in projects dealing with safety. Our highways slaughter thousands of humans every year. We are aghast to learn that the Aztecs sacrificed 20,000 humans annually, by a deliberate decision on the part of their priests. Yet we know that given our present safety measures, well over that figure will die on our highways. Indeed, we can estimate the dollar value of a slain auto driver in terms of the safety designs we are willing to implement on the highways.

The logical argument goes as follows: we are willing to pay $X to prevent fatal accidents: Y many fatal accidents will occur for each $X paid. Therefore, the "cost-value" of a fatal accident is $X divided by Y. You may be shocked by someone assigning a dollar value to a human life, but once the $X has been decided, the decision makers have implicitly decided on the dollar value; haven't they?

One most beware of the logician! Every time you find yourself trapped by an argument based on logic alone, you have the moral right to ask whether the whole trick is not based on a tautology. In this case, the tautology consists in defining "value" as "something to be maximized," a unifying concept. It follows from this definition that all free choices consist of a "trade-off" of one value for another, and that therefore there is a price for everything, including a life. But the human being may be influenced by other values which cannot be reduced to ego-drive desires. Indeed, we have already mentioned one such influence, the moral.

The Policy Choices with Respect to Wildlife

I can summarize what has been said thus far by listing the policy choices that are available to the Service whenever there appears to be a real conflict between humans and some other species.

1.   "Best of all possible worlds." This possibility occurs when, through research and subsequent implementation, we humans find a way of managing resources so that we give up very little if anything, and the wildlife is also virtually unharmed. The system of migratory bird refuges is an example. Without these refuges, strategically placed along the birds' pathways, we might well expect extinction of the pintail duck or the Canada goose. As it is, at relatively low cost, we humans can increase our own values by bird watching and managed hunting on the refuges, and the same time remove the danger to the bird species.

It should be pointed out that this policy "solution" may well be transitory; for example, a change in policy of the Canadians with respect to "pot holes", may again threaten the species. But more to the point, "best of all possible worlds" must be viewed within the relatively narrow limits of wildlife; the policy does not guarantee that the money spent on refuges could not better be spent on education or health or poverty.

2.   "The critters give way." This policy says that wildlife must suffer somewhat, so that highly desirable human goals can be attained. Examples are the coyote, the vampire bat and various insects in agricultural lands. The problem is "solved" by finding methods of killing the animals or insects which produce harm to sheep, cows, plants, etc. The argument (often not presented in articles describing a new killing technique) apparently goes as follows: humans are and should be the domi-

nating species because they can reason, conduct research, and control their environment in ways that no other species can even approximate. When a subset of a species threatens a very desirable human goal, and no "best of all possible worlds" solution can be found, then the threatening subset should be destroyed with due regard to costs and benefits, of course.

3.   "Humans give way." This policy is the essence of the Endangered Species Act. It says that in circumstances where the fulfillment of human desires threatens a wildlife species, then human desires must give way. As we humans developed the lands of the West to create new agricultural areas to feed ourselves, we wiped out the natural habitat of such birds as the whooping crane. Now, at whatever the cost may be, we ought to do our best to save the species from extinction.

Why? What impels us to this policy choice? I don't think the answer is "economic motivation", though I have no objection to people trying to find such a justification because the attempt may land us back in the "best of all possible worlds" solution. I think the justification is based on a moral and religious spirit that most of us humans share with respect to life — to all forms of living things. The remainder of this paper is an exploration of this idea. I'm not likely to find my evidence in planning theory or planning documents, like EIR's, but rather in spiritual and literary writings. I might add, as a forecaster, that I believe that the religious spirit with respect to wildlife is going to increase in the USA and possibly elsewhere; the Endangered Species Act, I hope, will be only one of many such decisions that are based on the religious spirit.

Moral Feelings

I think it is appropriate to call this religious spirit a "moral feeling", because it seems to speak through what C.G. Jung (1922) calls the feeling function. Morality touches us when we are morally outraged, say, at wanton killing, or selfish exploitation, but also when we are morally overjoyed by an act of kindness or caring.

My thesis is that we often are driven to act on the basis of moral feelings, which basis has little to do with objectives or maximization of some measure of performance. Such a thesis attacks the foundations of economics and operations research; one cannot appropriately express

moral feelings by writing a constraint equation in a mathematical program. One cannot do so, because once the constraint is written we can
infer a price for morality, which is inappropriate. Another way to say
the same thing is that there is no trade-off for committing evil: once
evil is done, it cannot be reduced by good acts. Only forgiveness dimin-
ishes evil.

Reason is a very strong human function; when reason is confronted
with a phenomenon, it naturally tries to explain it by subsuming it into
a larger picture. Now reason cannot deny that moral feelings exist; any
reading of a daily newspaper provides many examples of moral indignation, over poverty, pollution, exploitation, murder. Reason is impelled
to explain these moral feelings as well as to determine how much they
should influence rational decision making.

One obvious answer to reason's question about the origins of morality is to say that moral feelings come from our parents, teachers and other
guides of our youth. This is really not an explanation, because it leaves
open the question of the "endless" causal chain: how did our parents
and ancestors come by their morality? Perhaps a sounder explanation
is to be found in Hobbes (1651) and his theory of "biological condition-
ing": we are driven to social morality as a way of surviving.

Such explanations of human moral feelings are not very elevating.
In fact, my moral sense is repelled by them; they sound like the dry
utterances of men who have lost their own moral sense. Given a choice
of explanations, which seems to be the privilege of free inquiry, I much
prefer the explanation of men like Rousseau (1762) and Kant (1787).
For Kant, the self is not the ego alone; there is also the moral will which
operates not to attain goals, but rather by its own free legislation. The
Good Will is beyond cost-benefit motivation and similar "utilitarian"
motives; it is our most glorious inner gift. At the end of his *Critique
of Practical Reason,* Kant is ruminating about man's place in the immensity
of the universe, and summarizes his feelings thus: "two things fill my
heart with never ending awe: the starry heavens above and the moral
law within."

The law which each Will creates is never to treat another as means
only but as an end withal. It is to be emphasized that for Kant there is
no "reason" why we should obey this moral law, because to search for a

reason is to regard the moral law as purposive, goal-seeking, whereas the moral law stands on its own, so to speak.

Planners have tended to ignore Kant's message, and to be curiously indifferent to the outcries of moral sense. They are happiest when a problem can be fully posed as a search to obtain objectives. Yet a large number of plans consist of treating people as means only. I don't believe we can respond to moral sense by ignoring it. If a policy which supports a dictator results in severe hardship for the people, then we should judge it immoral, or at least debate its morality.

Nonetheless, I'm inclined to think that Kant over-rationalized the account of morality, because I think the truth is much simpler. I think that morality is the religious spirit within us which puts us in touch with our own species, humanity; it is the force which tells us how to be "natural" as human beings.

Morality is not often articulate because the moral sense does not often work through articulations, so that it is difficult to say in words what "being in touch with humanity" means. The best the rational mind can do, I think, is to use a concept like equity to come as near as it can to the meaning of the moral sense. Equity means fairness to all, that each individual is to be respected for his being, and that no individual or group of individuals is "more important" than any one person. The spirit is expressed in Matthew 25: "as you did it to one of the least of these, my brethren, you did it to me," or in Corinthians 13 where "love" is used to describe the spirit of being in touch with humanity. Paul is trying to say that without love the whole well planned enterprise of moving mountains, or, as we would put it today, of modern technology, is nothing. Wordsworth captures the same spirit at the end of his *Ode on Intimations of Immortality:* "to me the meanest flower that grows can give thoughts that do often lie too deep for tears."

Except that Wordsworth was not referring to humanity. Should we not say that the moral spirit puts us in touch with life? We could and we'd have plenty of eastern company: "the self is the fish born in water, the plant growing in earth" runs one of the *Upanishads.*

I have used these references to try to show that the thesis that moral sense puts us in touch with humanity and life is not new, although often we have to rediscover what our forebearers knew so well. Thus in the 1974 Winter issue of the *North American Review* are a series of articles on "non-human rights," in which the authors argue that humans should re-spect the rights of animals, plants and other forms of living beings. Most of the articles attack the assumption that man is the supreme species who is entitled to control nature in order to satisfy his own desires. They could well have quoted the *Bhagavad Gita:* "The seers say truly that he is wise who acts without lust or scheming for the fruit of the act — Turn-ing his face from the fruit, he needs nothing; the Atman is enough." (Book IV)

Lessons for Wildlife

Suppose for the moment we accept the thesis that morality is what puts us in touch with collective life. Suppose also that we should re-spond positively to our moral sense. Then haven't we found the basis for the Endangered Species Act? To destroy a species in order to satisfy our ego-desires is immoral, because it violates our human relationships to all life collectively. More narrowly, to destroy a species is immoral because it deprives all humankind in the future from relating to the destroyed species; hence the wanton destruction of a species ruins our sense of belonging to nature.

There is still a lot to be said even if we accept these suppositions. For example we have been talking about the right of a species to survive. Do we mean that all species should survive? And what about the indivi-duals of a species? Do they each have a right to survival?

On the first question, the reasonable answer seems to be "no", it is unnatural of us to intervene in a natural process of species extinction. Only if we can conclude that human intervention produced the decline of a species should we intervene to reverse what we started. This response is reasonable, but is it accurate? I don't know because I'm beyond my depth of knowledge: is it natural for a species to bring about the de-struction of another species? (It is estimated that humanity produces between a four-fold and an eight-fold increase in species extinction when it moves into an area.) Or, having by its acts dangerously reduced the size of a species, is it natural for a species to try to prevent the total destruction? Finally, is it natural for a species which has the capability of preserving a dangerously threatened species to do so, even if it was not the cause of the decline?

These questions are all germane to our wildlife policy with respect to the whooping crane. The justification for our policy must be in a negative response to the first question (it is unnatural for a species to destroy another species), or an affirmative answer to the second or third (it is natural to intervene if we have been the cause, or if we have the capability of preservation).

I can find no reasonable objections to the first and second of these responses, provided we recognize the reasonableness of the questions. I have used the word "wanton" in describing some of our historical destructions of species; the word means "undisciplined," and specifically in this case a lack of disciplined reasoning: our forefathers gave no thought to the long-range meaning of their acts. In ignoring the value of species, they lacked a sense of good management of human affairs. Thus if we have wantonly endangered a species, it may very well be natural for us to right the wrong of wanton management and seek to preserve it.

As to the third question, my own reasoning can find no powerful justification of it: just because we are capable of preserving a species seems no reason why we should do so, else we'd be caught in the intolerable absurdity of saying that we ought to do those things we are capable of doing. But perhaps we could respond affirmatively by introducing that very powerful and natural feeling called compassion. If a species is dying, should we not act out of compassion for its plight? The question has taken us to that age-old moral issue of euthanasia. Doesn't compassion also say that we should let the pained die in peace? But, of course, the whooping crane is not in pain. I think reason has now come to its limit: the question must be answered by the spirit. If our spiritual feeling for the crane says "save it!" then we should respond to the cry and compassionately help our fellow living being.

What should be said about individual rights? Do I have the right to kill a house fly, eat a chicken, shoot a poisonous snake? We all know how far the absurdity of concern for killing can go. A friend of mine used to feel along the edge of a door before closing it, lest he crush a bug. Vegetarians become embarrassed when their teasers claim that plants have feelings.

One response to the question is to say that "cruel" killing of individuals is unnatural, and indeed we recognize the appeal of this response in our laws restraining cruelty to animals. Another response is to say that humans are the only species concerned about individual mortality and immortality; the claim is that all the other species act as though the collective life of the species is all that matters. I'm never sure how humans decide what differentiates them from other species; I am sure that we are the only species which concerns itself with this issue. Hence I'm dubious about the second response. I believe that we have a great deal to learn about individual rights, both in our own species and in others. It will be some time before we can formulate rational policies with respect to living individuals, and perhaps the issue lies beyond reason. In any event, each of us must respond as best he can with respect to individual living beings by listening to the spiritual voice.

Non-Living Rights

Before turning to the problem of the justification of the thesis of this paper, I should mention that writers both ancient and modern speak of the rights of the non-living. Perhaps the moral sense that puts us in touch with humanity and more generally life, extends also to all reality — the rocks and mountains, for example. The quotation I gave from the *Upanishads* also says that "the Self is the sun shining in the sky, the wind blowing in space . . ." and Book IV of the *Bhagavad Gita* takes up the same theme: "Brahman is the ritual, Brahman is the offering, Brahman is he who offers to the fire that is Brahman." Such reflections may be more germane to the Bureau of Reclamation and the Army Corps of Engineers than they are to the Fish and Wildlife Service.

Justification

Perhaps the reader will feel that this paper has touched fantasy rather than reality. Certainly my friends who wonder what future generations had ever done for them would find most of the discussion lacking in reality. Then there are those who are impressed by the vagueness and contradictoriness of the moral sense, which speaks thus to some people and non-thus to others. A hunter is excited by the act of shooting a wild beast but the anti-hunter is horrified. A recent film shows grown men shooting at buffalo who stand innocently in a field, while some renegade boys are shocked into radical action. All this elicits the sophomoric "different strokes for different folks!"

Of course, the thesis of this paper is a speculation; but so is moral relativism. Nature rarely communicates with us in consistent terms, and it is only by dint of very hard work that we can begin to understand who we are and the world we live in.

It has taken us a long time to realize that wanton killing is morally wrong, and we still don't realize the immensity of this realization. Further, there are many of us who don't realize it yet, who have no feeling for future generations or other forms of life, except in terms of egoistic cost-benefit analysis. I don't know how to argue with them, partly because they themselves prefer not to argue; their relativism is incredibly entrenched.

My justification of the thesis is as much religious and aesthetic, as it is intellectual. To be in touch with humanity and life is an aesthetic experience. It is also a religious experience. And since it is both, the experience is largely inarticulate: one can at best use symbols and analogies rather than "operationally defined" terms. It may be as Paul put it in the quotation at the beginning of this paper, "For as in one body we have many members, and all members have not the same function; so we, being many, are yet one body in Christ (God, Krisna, Jehovah) and every one members one of another." It is also perhaps, as Maximus of Tyre put it: "God Himself, the Father and Fashioner of all that is, older than the Sun and the Sky, greater than Time and Eternity and all the Flow of Being, is unnameable by any Lawgiver, unutterable by any Voice, not to be seen by any Eye — If a Greek is stirred to remembrance of God by the art of Phidias, an Egyptian by paying worship to animals, another man by a river, another by a fire, I have no anger for their divergences. Only let them know, let them love, let them remember."

7

SOME NOTES ON THE ORGANIZATION OF
EXOTERIC UNIVERSITIES*

Prologue

In the long history of attempts to prove Euclid's Parallel Postulate, one of the most ingenious goes as follows: Imagine that you are at point A in the triangle ABC, facing directly down the line AB. You proceed to B where you make a left turn to face down the line BC. Then on your cheerful way to C, make another left turn down CA, and finally arriving at A, turn left again to face B. The journey

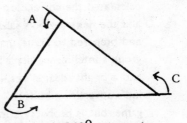

obviously has turned you completely around through 360°. At each turning point you have turned through 180° minus the adjacent interior angle of the triangle. A little simple arithmetic proves that the sum of the three interior angles must therefore be 180°, i.e., two right angles.

---

*   Presented at the seminar on "Organizations of the Future," in Holland, August 31-September 4, 1970.

It is known that one can deduce Euclid's Parallel Postulate from the proposition that the sum of the angles of a triangle are equal to two right angles. QED.

But what this ingenious geometrician did was not to prove that space is Euclidean, but rather that Euclidean is an interesting space, one in which we can make turns in any part of the plane and regard their sum as though the turns took place at one point. This is one example of the remarkable invariance properties of Euclidean space. In the non-Euclidean geometry which Saccheri dubbed the Hypothesis of the Acute, the amount of turning the trip requires is always greater than the amount required if you stay at home at point A, and can entail as much as one and a half times as much effort.

Without attempting to be needlessly precise, I'd like to introduce the label "reasoning inversion" for the incident just described. Reason, which sets out to prove that space is Euclidean, later on gets inverted into the proposition that Euclidean is a kind of space. Reasoning inversion is some sort of turning the picture around, usually accompanied by surprise as well as a bit of learning.

Reasoning inversion often plays its tricks in causal analysis. Ackoff tells the story of an Operations Research team which recommended a reduction in a company's advertising expenditures. The firm's advertising agency got wind of the proposed recommendation and set their statistician to work to show that the proposal was unsound. The statistician calculated the correlation between one period's advertising expenditure and the next period's sales, and came up with the impressive figure 0.94, and prepared to argue that advertising causes higher sales. The OR group's intelligence department learned of this foray, and one of them had a bright idea: "Let's correlate one period's sales with the next period's advertising budget!" The result was 0.99, which not only won the game, but is probably a more accurate account of how the causal chain went: management reacted to sales by adjusting advertising. This reasoning inversion is probably quite common in management practice; for example, the R and D groups with the best payoffs get the most funding, so that success causes funding rather than funding causing success.

What relevance, if any, this little excursion into inversion may have will have to wait for the Eiplogue.

The subject of this chapter is a desirable way to organize exoteric universities. "Exoteric" is an esoteric name for "suitable to the general public" rather than a special class (e.g., the learned of a discipline) which characterizes "esoteric." Exoteric universities are primarily interested in generating knowledge which will be helpful in solving society's problems, where "solving" means "improving social conditions" rather than removing all difficulties.

It should be noted that I am not really interested in forecasting what university organizations will be like in the future, because I find that exercise ranges from fruitless to depressing depending on how it is done. It is fruitless if we adopt the world view that universities are remarkably resilient institutions which will adapt to various pressures while maintaining their great traditions of learning. It is depressing if we love our university but realize that it is caught in a vice, one side of which is propelled by legislators and the conservative public, the other by radical students.

My personal style of inquiry leans toward trying to say what kind of university organization would seem best for the task, in this case the task of generating socially valuable knowledge, and then to speculate on how such an organization might be created.

We can begin by saying some things about the organization of esoteric universities, in order to make some contrasts. Perhaps the extreme of the esoteric is experimental physics; I understand that a graduate student should expect to spend at least three years in study before he can be in a position to run meaningful experiments. In such universities the traditional departmental organization, together with its required courses, seems eminently sensible. The basic model is one of information transmittal in its most general sense, where information means not only factual and theoretic materials but also techniques and methods. The information is contained in the minds of a few people, who are practiced in the art of transmittal. Furthermore, these people are best qualified to determine when the student is capable of producing new information on his own. The esoteric unversity requires an administration to provide the needed resources, and a public or patron to provide the funding.

To be sure, esoteric universities do have a basic weakness from the exoteric point of view, because no one outside the privileged class can adequately decide whether the education is worthwhile. All the public can see is an occasional surprising and delightful "breakthrough," like a polio vaccine, but then it also sees surprising and horrible breakthroughs, like biological warfare. De Morgan in his *Budget of Paradoxes* tells us of the amateur theologian who claimed that God created centripetal force to counteract centrifugal force; De Morgan's remark, "Why didn't God let well enough alone," might equally apply to the public in today's scientific society. The point seems to be that on any reasonable grounds esoteric universities should be judged on exoteric grounds. But this seems to pose a paradox, because only in esoteric universities, like medical, engineering and law schools, can useful social knowledge be generated.

Philosophers love paradoxes because they are invitations to their most cherished recreation: defining. So let's recreate by trying to define "useful social knowledge." Here there seems to be no great difficulty. Imagine that you wish to attain some goal, but are not very effective in its pursuit. I come in and state proposition p; you respond to my statement by choosing a much more effective means to your desired end. Then it seems reasonable to say that proposition p is "useful knowledge" for you.*

If we apply this idea to the exoteric university, it suggests a kind of production and distribution model. The university, say, is in the business of producing the p's which when retrieved by members of the public makes them more effective in the pursuit of their ends. This in fact is the idea underlying the application of cost-benefit analysis to education.

We can begin to see how the esoteric university can be organized to have and eat its cake. It uses the traditional organization of disciplines to produce esoteric knowledge, but it also educates people who study the market. These practicing doctors, engineers, etc., are sufficiently aware of both the meaning of the esoteric knowledge and the public's needs to make the match that yields socially useful knowledge. In the design, the young person with ambition to practice undergoes so-and-so many years having esoteric knowledge fed into him or her, and at

---

* The idea needs further amplification because we need to decide whether sentence p needs to be a declarative sentence in order to be useful knowledge, since it could be a command, an epithet, or whatever. But such amplification would divert the thought pattern too much at this point.

some point leaves the esoteric to become exoteric.

But there are a number of weaknesses in this arrangement. For one thing, the burden on the practicing professions may be very great, because they must keep abreast of the esoteric findings and the changes in public need. But the more serious weakness has been mentioned above, namely, that the public may not know what it needs. For example, the public says it needs to move around faster, so the practicing engineer applies some theory to develop the internal combustion engine which pollutes the air. It turns out that the public's needs are all highly coupled, so that satisfying one need very well may spell disaster for another need.

The esoteric university has responded to this "systems" problem by trying to develop another kind of knowledge, variously labeled systems analysis, operations research, management science, etc. The same organizational design has been applied here as well. One group produces esoteric knowledge about "whole systems," mathematical models, simulations, utility measurements, and so on. The practitioners then try to apply this esoteric knowledge to "real" problems in order to avoid the evils of blindly pursuing one goal. To be sure, at the present time the applications turn out to be crude, but perhaps no cruder than applied medicine at the present time.

It is noteworthy that university personnel have adapted the traditional pattern of organization to the growing need for social reform without giving much consideration at all to its appropriateness.

Now a principle of organizational design that's not bad says that whenever you succeed in ferreting out an obvious but not examined assumption (by no means an easy task!), then confront it with a plausible view of why it is wrong. In the case of the design of exoteric universities, the obvious assumption has already been challenged. The observant student of systems analysis complains that the esoteric models and theories of utility have no relevance to him and that when he graduates he still has no idea what operations research is all about. As for the experienced manager, he often regards the efforts of the academically trained systems analyst to range from impudent to imprudent. Then there is the activist who wants to do and not to think; for him, the planner and systems expert are in an alliance with the establishment to delay change by one more study.

It is of interest to turn to business schools in the context of this discussion. A number of years ago three experts, Gordon, Howell and Pearson, criticized busincess schools for the weak material presented in the curriculum. In effect, the two reports challenged the schools to become more esoteric in economics, mathematics and behavioral science. Many of them accepted the challenge. Did they become any "better" as a result? They are probably more respected by the esoteric community, but a good case could be made that the revolution in business education did not increase and may have weakened their exoteric power.

The world view which argues against the traditional design of university organizations is easy enough to state. It says, in the case of the systems analyst, that his esoteric knowledge, and not reality, shapes his formulation of the problem. Since it does, he can't even recognize some of the critical features of the problem, and is all too apt to believe that the manager is stupid. In particular, he fails to see human feelings, political power, anxiety, and all similar realities of the organization. Of course, the student who got his esoteria from the behavioral scientist does see some of these things, but he, lacking the mathematics, fails to see the underlying logic.

All of the above are familiar complaints, but what do they tell us about designing the exoteric university in another way? Well, first they tell us that the university is not the only place which is producing "socially useful knowledge." Every organization produces useful knowledge of a very general sort. The ghetto dweller is as much an expert as the university dweller.

Next, not only do other organizations and people produce socially useful knowledge, but they also produce useful methods of inquiry into organizational problems. These methods differ from the esoteric methods of hypothesis and validation, but they are just as reliable. They tend to rely more heavily than the esoteric on intuition, general experience, and human feelings. The methods are remarkably diverse, as though each person has his own individual style of inquiry.

Finally, the traditional design of esoteric universities makes a sharp differentiation between its form of knowledge and all other forms and methods. But even from its own esoteric concept of a system, this differentiation may be entirely wrong, because it assumes that the university is a separable component of the social system. As the students are telling us, excellent production of esoteric knowledge does not imply that the whole social system benefits.

Consider, now, an alternative design of an exoteric university, one which tries to encompass the whole production system of socially useful knowledge. This one works something like an organized religion, though there aren't any priests or bishops in the usual sense. The university is a consortium of people and organizations whose main purpose is to generate socially useful knowledge. The organizations include churches, government agencies, labor unions, firms, etc. Legislatures recognize the need to inquire and might even convert their hearings into university departments.

The university, in this design, is not all organizations and people, but only those who have a sufficient need to join. The "need to join" is based on an individual or organizational desire to develop one's style of inquiry by acquiring more information or refining methodology or whatever. The criterion of admission is not based on academic performance, though this may be the basis for some departments. Each member organization regards itself as having a dual function, its own task and its educational task. Its educational policy is formulated in terms of its own specific needs; there are no general university policies regarding courses, merit and the rest. But the university does control certain facilities, like libraries, computers and certain research centers, where the returns to scale so warrant; in such cases general university policy does apply.

A number of problems that are central to the esoteric university become minor or transformed in this design of an exoteric university. Since merit is not the main criterion for admission or completion, the university does not have to concern itself with admission standards or degree certification, although member organizations may concern themselves with these matters. Indeed, some of the departments of an esoteric university (physics, medicine, etc.) might operate under the policies of the exoteric university, with required courses, examinations, etc.

On the other hand, the university is deeply concerned with the question of who should belong and when a person or organization should no longer belong, because the university's central concern is with the process of maturation of the individual style of inquiry. Its central problem, therefore, is how the university can and cannot aid in this process. One would expect to find an important part of the university's research effort devoted to this issue.

Evidently, to spell out in detail how such an organization might work would require a book, or several. The following are some notes to suggest the topics such a dissertation might cover.

Funding. In our culture, it is almost obvious that people should pay for services received, though the payment need not always be monetary. So I suppose that one should pay to become and continue to be a member of the university. But within the university community, the organizations should have their own policies of payment as well as membership. For example, a firm might belong to the university with the explicit purpose of using the university as its management development program. Other organizations of the university might then provide the managers various courses, or weeks of experience in banking, real estate, etc. The payment for the inter-organizational arrangements would be up to the individual organizations; the university would require payment for admittance of individual managers.

Administration. My strong inclination is to bring about a "withering away" of the prestige of university administration. The job of running the university should be just that — a job. Deans and presidents might still be required but would be regarded much as any other member is regarded. One way to accomplish this would be to have the university contract its administration to a company, where the contract holds over a specific time period, and renewal is based on past performance.

Governance. It is easy to say that the governance of the university should be "democratic" but impossible to say, at the present time, what this should mean. One of the first research projects of the university should be the study of how universities should be governed. Until such research bears fruit, the university should experiment with different constitutions. One design might be modeled on the USA Constitution. It would have several weaknesses, one of which is that the constitution does not provide for its own dissolution.

Learning Center. The heart of the exoteric university is its learning center which serves the function of helping each of the members to learn about himself as an "inquiring system".* It serves the same function as grades, examinations, and course evaluations but in a much deeper manner. It tries to help each member to inquire about the design of his life in as rich a fashion as possible. It also helps each member decide whether he should leave the University or stay with it for another period. Those who continuously receive the message "don't leave" are called "the faculty". Finally, it is not clear whether the learning center is a location and a typical administrative organization, or not.

Politics and Academic Freedom. "Academic freedom" is a value for the esoteric university but probably a hindrance to the exoteric university. Certainly politics will be a critical factor in an organization devoted to producing socially valuable knowledge. The University community, for example, should probably support certain reform measures for local, state, and national governments, or bond issues, candidates, etc. Here again is a topic for university research effort: what political role should an exoteric university play?

Organization. Tentatively (very), the university is composed of the following:

1.   Individual members: anyone who believes he has a need for development which the university can supply, and who pays the university's price, plus a minimum of additional constraints on admittance;

2.   Organizational members, with equally open admittance criteria. Some of these organizations are directly tied into the university as an entity. These include the administration, esoteric curricula, university-oriented research of the type described above, and centers for the study of individual styles of inquiry.

3.   A governing body which decides on policy.

Feeling. One of the major characteristics of the university should be the creation of a strong positive "feeling institution," similar in kind to successful religions, unions, orders and firms. A feeling institution is one in which there is a good feeling attached to belonging. To get the idea, compare the feeling of a liberal intellectual in being a citizen of the USA in 1900 and in 1970. The feeling has gone from good to bad

---

*   C. West Churchman, *The Design of Inquiring Systems,* NY: Basic Books, 1971.

for many of them. Just how one creates a good feeling of belonging to
an institution is simple: just find the good people to do it! Which plati-
tude brings me to the

Epilogue

We can see that it is extremely reasonable to argue that people need
to participate in communities in order to solve social problems: poverty,
pollution, and population, say. Now try out reasoning inversion on this
reasonable axiom of social planning. What emerges is that we need to
create social problems in order to get people to participate together.
Participation is the fundamental value, and problem solving is the optimal means of bringing it about. Pollution and poverty would not exist
as problems if we did not make them so; we make them so in order to
share together a common concern. This bit of reasoning inversion says
that it is always a good idea to invert means and ends: thereby you get
a whole new Weltanschauung of the community.

8

FORTY YEARS IN MEASURING HUMAN VALUES

This chapter is not intended to be a history of the attempts to measure human values over the past forty years, but rather of my own involvement in the problem; so, much of what was truly valuable that was produced during the period may well be omitted. The chapter was partially inspired by one of the students in my Ph.D. seminar at Berkeley. His topic was the measurement of consumer satisfaction. At the beginning, he remarked that behavioral studies in this area dated back to the early 1960's, at which point I rather indignantly pointed out to him that I had helped run a conference and edit a book on the measurement of consumer interest in the mid-1940's.[25] I don't think he was much impressed; he probably thought that anything written before that Age of Enlightenment called the 1960's would surely be obscurely medieval in character.

---

25. The conference was held at the University of Pennsylvania in 1946, and the book, *Measurement of Consumer Interest* (ed. by C.W. Churchman, R.L. Ackoff, and M. Wax) was published by the University of Pennsylvania Press in 1947.

Actually (according to my bias), the book is an amazingly informative, interdisciplinary approach to the topic, having papers by statisticians, pollsters, marketing experts, the head of the Consumer Union, and philosophers. Guttman made one of his earliest presentations on his method of scaling preferences.

At that time, I was hard at work with Russell Ackoff in our attempt to define concepts of psychology, sociology, and ethics, which appeared in 1946 under the title *Psychologistics* (mimeographed). My paper in the consumer interest conference volume was mainly concerned, not with the question of measuring a consumer's satisfaction with a product or service, but with the legitimacy of his interest, i.e., with the claims he legitimately ought to be able to make for goods and services in a society. This effort was in the spirit of the conference, which had other papers dealing with consumer rights.

During the period of the '40's, I spent a great deal of time trying to understand the calibration process of measuring human values. As mentioned in Part I, during World War II, I had worked on the calibration of measurements in the physical sciences (mainly, physical chemistry and metallurgy). All of the measurement processes were out of control in the sense that independent observers reported significantly different results. I realized that what E.A. Singer had taught me was very important in any measurement procedure, namely, calibration, or bringing independent findings into statistical control. Compared to the difficulty of this task, attempts at modeling preference structures are child's play.

The reason why calibration is so difficult is that there is no straightforward way of proceeding. Independent observers differ significantly in their findings because the environments of the measurements are different or the observers themselves differ. The usual way of handling the problem is to specify a "standard" environment and observer. But, of course, one has to be able to measure the critical properties of the environment and the observers; and these measurements also require standards. In short, the calibration procedure is cyclical: one assumes that standards are met for one type of measurement in order to measure something else, and then assumes the second standards are met in order to measure a third, and so on, returning eventually to correcting the first.

I can illustrate the calibration circle by supposing we'd like to measure Mr. X's values of convenience, comfort, and expense in buying a house. Suppose we show him several sets of house drawings, locations, and prices and ask him to make choices. We'd surely have to assume that he can tell from the drawings and other data how comfortable, convenient, and economical each house is. That is, we assume a degree of knowledge as part of the standard. Further, Mr. X may have this thing about stained-glass windows, which, if they appear in the drawings, completely sway his choice. We assume that there are no such "things" in Mr. X's case. But if we set out to check our two assumptions about knowledge and "things" in the house that control choice, we find that we have to assume some properties of Mr. X's values. For example, I can't check your knowledge of means to an end unless I assume you have a real interest in the end.

I need to emphasize that the circular property of calibration is not vicious; as the history of the measurement of white light *in vacuo* shows[26], progress can be made.

It was in the early 1950's that I began facing some of the really serious and practical issues of measuring human values. I had become fascinated by the possibility of applying some of the optimal decision-making models that had been developed earlier in the century to help manage inventory and replacement systems. Having been a student of E.A. Singer, Jr., I realized that the critical problem was not so much in the modeling as in the measurement of the parameters of the model. This realization continues to be rare among operations researchers; the basic texts in OR rarely tell the student how to acquire data and use it to measure the coefficients in the model.

In most of the models, the critical measurement is what economists call "opportunity costs". To summarize the argument given in Part I, opportunity costs mean the loss one incurs in *not* doing x because one has done y, x and y being mutually exclusive. Thus if I purchase and hold in inventory items totalling $100,000, I give up the

---

26.   In the 1700's, the probable error was several thousands of km/sec.; today, the probable error is less than 0.1 km/sec.

opportunity of using the money for other purposes. The determination of opportunity costs is essential in the application of all OR models.

When we examine the calibration process for measuring opportunity costs, the magnitude of the task becomes apparent. If I don't purchase $100,000 worth of items, what else can I do with the money and what will be the net return? But this is not the correct version of the calibration question, which should read: What is the *optimal* use of the money? After all, I may be a stupid investor. To answer the correct question, I need a cash-flow model. The cash-flow model requires, for its calibration, the overall policy model for the firm's investments and operations. The little old purchasing agent's worry about how many items to purchase for inventory requires for its answering a financial model of the firm.

Most texts in OR make no mention of how to measure opportunity costs; or, if they do, they make simple-minded assumptions (e.g., putting the $100,000 into high-interest loans, as though the firm's best policy is to become a loan company).

Of course, the innocent may think that accountants collect opportunity-cost information; but they do nothing of the kind. We (Ackoff and I) thought that those who taught "managerial accounting" would have to teach measurement methods for opportunity costs and eagerly wrote an article for the *Journal of Accountancy* which we called "Operational Accounting" (1955). It fell into the puddle of accounting literature with hardly a ripple.

I feel the need to state the thesis on the calibration of opportunity costs somewhat differently from the way I did it in Part I. It seems to me that there are two choices. One could argue that the lost opportunity is to be costed in terms of what the manager would do with the released funds, and this choice on the part of the researcher would keep the problem bounded because one could ask him, or infer from his past behavior. The second choice is the one I have adopted, which argues that one must try to estimate the optimal use of the released funds, which implies that the problem becomes unbounded. The first choice provides us with a descriptive account of opportunity costs, the second with a prescriptive account. Since we planners are in the prescriptive business, it seems clear to me that the second choice is the only reasonable one. Perhaps this point becomes more forceful if we look at another measure of inventory control, the demand on inventory. Most textbooks tell the student to fit a histogram to data on past demands, and hence in effect choose the first option. But this really doesn't make good sense at all, because often the company can change demand by advertising and/or pricing; for example, manufacturers of harvest equipment often adopt a policy of seasonal pricing in order to smoothe out demand. This means that they must move from the inventory model to a marketing model and thence into financial considerations. But if one can improve the whole system by redesigning the marketing subsystem, it would be foolish to argue doggedly that the problem is inventory.

Despite the theoretical difficulties in measuring opportunity costs, we still practice OR. What we do, in effect, is to design a court procedure where the problem of the appropriate value of an opportunity cost is debated between managers and OR professionals. There is no guarantee that the court's judgment is correct, any more than there is for any other court's judgments; but at least this procedure is feasible. It does "quantify" human values, but in the strict sense it does not measure them.

For some of our practical work, in the mid-1950's Ackoff and I invented a technique we called an "approximate" measure of value. To use our method, one had to assume not only the simple structure of preferences (e.g., asymmetry and transitivity), but also additivity ("If on some scale, O_1 has a value V_1 and O_2, a value V_2, then O_1 - and - O_2 has a value $V_1 + V_2$"). People were asked to rank a set of objectives and then assign 1 to the highest ranked and "suitable" lesser numbers to the rest. They then used the additivity assumption to check the results (e.g., if O_2 is valued at .8 and O_3 at .4, then O_2 - and - O_3 should be valued above O_1; if not, the numbers are to be adjusted).

I think now that we had a lot of nerve calling our method "approximate", as though it were in a series of closer and closer approximations to the true values of the objectives. I'd dare say today that no set of objectives are even approximately additive. For one thing, the "and" is highly ambiguous; for another, all objectives are strongly nonseparable. Finally, as I've argued in Part I, it's very questionable whether objectives can be ranked since transitivity probably doesn't hold.

Nevertheless, I did apply the method "successfully". There was a

firm in Cleveland run by three brothers who had inherited it from their
father. One of the brothers wanted to take on a large Air Force contract that would have doubled the gross return. Another brother was
against the idea because it would mean a large capital investment and subsequent financial risk. The third worried about the firm's responsibility
to older employees who had worked with the "old man" at the beginning.
We got the three together to begin defining as precisely as possible the
firm's objectives of (1) gaining by financial opportunities, (2) remaining
financially secure, (3) guaranteeing employment for key personnel, and
a number of other objectives. They then independently ranked and assigned value numbers to the objectives*, and afterwards met to discuss
the results. At first the results were quite different; after the meeting,
they redid the assignment. At the end, they were remarkably close.

I don't really think the method "measured" their values, but it
did succeed in removing their conflicts. Some objectives that had re-
peatedly been mentioned in earlier discussions were clearly quite unimportant relative to the top-ranking objectives. The brothers learned a
lot about each other by partaking in the assignment.

This may seem an odd conclusion, but it taught me what I'll make
the conclusion of this paper, namely, that the process of trying to quantify human values may teach us a lot about people. I certainly learned
something important about myself when I used the "approximate"
method in trying to decide whether to take a job at Berkeley or Michigan State. I stated a number of objectives (salary, colleagues, environment, etc.) and followed through the process, with the conclusion that
I should choose Michigan State. I'd left out the "thing" business: there
are no "stained-glass windows" in East Lansing, but the Bar Area has
them everywhere.

In the early '60's, I decided to try to review all published efforts
to quantify human values. I expected to find most of them in three
areas, accounting, economics, and philosophy; and I named the review
Costs, Utilities and Values. [27]

---

*   If independent rankers assign numbers, one has to normalize the results.
27.   Subsequently published as *Prediction and Optimal Decision,* Prentice
Hall, 1963.

Accounting should be assigning quantities to human values, and in some sense it does, but it also performs various rituals and helps managers in their political activities. In order to clarify in my own mind just what accounting should do, I constructed an axiom set for accounting procedures. This idea started off a whole series of efforts on the part of academic accountants to find the fundamental axioms. I have the feeling that the efforts were strictly academic, but they were a lot of fun, and for a while I found myself having a great time with a group of people who called themselves "accounting theorists".

As for economics, I was well aware of the philosophical struggle that went into founding utilitarianism (with its quantification of "utilities") in the eighteenth century. Utility is a more general measure than money, since there seems to be overwhelming evidence that the quantity of value in a process is not linear in money. In some sense, Hume was more sophisticated than Bentham because the latter tried to use pleasure-pain as the foundation, whereas the former based his value theory on the ability to attain goals. As everyone knows who has tried to measure pleasure, it's a very slippery phenomenon. Even the process of measurement ("How intensely are you enjoying this occasion?") may wipe out the pleasure.

On the other hand, the measurement of utility seems quite promising just because it can be related to money. The philosophical question is this: What does the measure of utilities tell us about basic human values? If one answers this question by saying, "All there is to know", one has adopted utilitarianism. But of course the philosopher doesn't stop there. Why should one say anything of the kind? And even if one does say such a thing, does one mean the human values of all society or just each person's own values? For example, Bentham begins his *Introduction to the Principles of Morals and Legislation* by saying that seeking pleasure and avoiding pain are fundamental drives of all humans; but within several pages, he's talking about the greatest pleasure for the greatest number. Pleasure-pain may on occasion determine my own choices. But why should the greatest pleasure for the greatest number drive me at all? Utilitarianism has never been able to find a sound proof that we humans should move from the micro to the macro. Sidgwick[28],

_____

28. *Methods of Ethics,* 1874.

rather naively, thought this move to be an intuitively clear postulate of morality.

As to whether all human values are based on utilities, the answer seems very obvious. As E.A. Singer put it, "With only one wish to be had, choose rather the power to get whatever you may come to want than the pleasure of having any dearest thing in the world." In *The Systems Approach and Its Enemies* (1979, pp. 137-8), I argue that this statement, which says that we humans above all want the ability (utility) to satisfy all our wants, is a tautology.

Over the years I've known economists, I've heard a number of them assert with conviction that economics is free of philosophical issues. I really don't know who in authority made this strange assertion that so many economists of this generation accept. If (theoretical) economics is based on utilitarianism, they seem to believe that there's no need to worry about the fact that there's no sound way to go from personal values to social values and that the foundation of the discipline is a tautology. After all, in that rather strange period around 1900, David Hilbert thought that arithmetic was a "grand" tautology. The trouble is that we poor humans have to use theoretical economics and arithmetic in our daily lives. Is our use of these disciplines based solely on the arbitrary definition of terms? What nonsense!

In the book, I point out that a tautology may be, not a foundation, but the initiator of a stream of good ideas. But when this happens, the tautology must wither away and be replaced. So I returned to the question: Is the quality of being useful for attaining goals the basic value of all actions and things for human beings?

As I've mentioned elsewhere in this book, the negative response to this question was being formulated in one of its most forceful forms in the same decade that saw Bentham designing utilitarianism. It was Kant [29] who argued that the only thing that is "good-in-itself" is the good will. I've covered this idea in detail elsewhere. [30] Essentially, Kant's position is that we humans should be governed by one moral law, the best formulation of which is: never treat humanity either in yourself or in

29.   *Foundations of the Metaphysics of Morals* (1785).
30.   *The Systems Approach and Its Enemies*, ch. 6

others as means only, but as an end withal.

For the sake of brevity, I merely want to summarize my own convictions at the present time about Kant's theory and its relevance to quantifying basic human values.

1.   Kant's theory of morality does not permit gradations of morality in human actions and, hence in this sense, does not permit quantification of the moral quality of an act.

2.   There is no "trade-off" principle in Kant's theory: one cannot "buy off" evil by subsequently doing good.

3.   The most serious problems we face today (poverty, militarism, pollution, etc.) are all equity problems in Kant's sense and are *not* based on economic considerations of low productivity.*

In closing these historical notes about the quantification of human values, I'd like to return to the concept of preference. Even though a knowledge of human preferences may not catch the central idea behind ethical judgments, a knowledge of preferences may be quite useful in formulating social policies. Here I find two difficulties, one technical, the other theoretical.

One technical difficulty I discussed in Part I, namely whether "a is preferred to b" is transitive. Now suppose we examine asymmetry. Suppose an individual has chosen a instead of b; then he himself has changed because of his choice and may have so changed that he now chooses b over a. For example, when the fruit platter is passed, he may choose an orange instead of a banana; but on the next passing, he may choose the banana. One could not infer that he is indifferent between oranges and bananas, but merely that the memory of having already eaten an orange makes him prefer the banana.

One might try to avoid this technical difficulty by setting up a "standard" where the individual has no memory of past choices. But he surely has to know what oranges and bananas taste like, else his choice is, at best, random. Nor is the difficulty eased by just asking him, because the oral response to a question may also alter the preference.

I suspect that the right approach to the technical difficulties of

_____

*   Many people today would call the statements "Marxist", but I much prefer to give the credit to their real philosophical inventor, Kant.

quantifying preferences is to recognize that there are "subspecies" of preferences. One species is quite stable over time (e.g., comfort vs. discomfort), another changes significantly over time (choice of fruits), another simply does not permit meaningful comparison (Which of your children do you prefer over the others?). There is really no good reason to expect that the changing types order any set of goals, nor do the incomparables.

I call this difficulty "technical", to imply that perhaps there are technical solutions to it, e.g., a better classification of preferences. But my theoretical question is much more serious. I said earlier that any measurer has to ask himself what he does to the object being measured and its environment. Now when I ask X whether he prefers a to b, what do I do to him? And what happens to his mind once the question is posed?

In the recent literature of psychology, there have been many proposals for "mapping" the human mind.[31] Freud had one of the earliest: the mind has both a conscious and an unconscious area, and, as force-fields, the id, ego, and superego. So in this mapped area, how do we locate where my preference question lands? The most likely response is in the conscious ego. What does "I prefer a to b" mean? It means that when these words are uttered, they come from the area of X's mind called the conscious ego, which is capable of forming the oral responses "a" or "b". What of the rest of the mind? What does it mean to say, "X prefers a to b"? Certainly not that X's "mind" has any such preference (as though residents of Brooklyn could speak for the whole of New York City).

The "map" of the mind is a metaphor, of course. But it is helpful in understanding how psychologically simplistic the study of preferences has been in utility measures, game theory, negotiation theory, consumer preferences, etc. If one asks which candidate the citizens of the USA "prefer" for their president, it would certainly be naive to say that it's the candidate the majority of those who voted, voted for. The great "unconscious" majority probably agreed with Ambrose Bierce's

---

31.   For a summary of some of these, see Charles Hampden-Turner's **Maps of the Mind** (1981)

definition: "president, n., a group of persons of whom it may safely be said that the great majority of the citizens do not want them to be president."

I don't want to stop the academic urge to play games with preferences, nor do I expect my remarks to stop them anyway. But perhaps it would be helpful to us observers if they said, "The 'people' we're theorizing about exist in only one rather odd part of humans' minds."

At the end, I can honestly say that the attempt to measure human values is a great idea because one learns so much about human nature by trying. Those opposed to the idea miss so much.

9

PHILOSOPHICAL NOTES
ON PUBLIC PARTICIPATION

We can begin by recognizing once again the ethical foundation of
the USA: that government by the "common people" is the highest form
of government humans can design. The Greek word for people gives
us "demo" and the Greek word for government gives us "cracy":
"democracy." It is not quite adequate to say that the citizens of the
United States live in a democracy, but it is accurate to say, as Lincoln
did, that we live in a democratic experiment ("testing whether that
nation or any nation so conceived and so dedicated can long endure").
I don't mean that we are performing this experiment in a clear, coherent manner because we often allow greed, exploitation, suppression and
bureaucratic politics to contaminate our experiment. But the ideal of
governance by the people still exists as forcibly in 1982 as it did in
1776 and 1863.

As a philosopher, I regard the Declaration of Independence to be
an expression of the democratic ideal, whereas I regard the Constitution
of the United States to be one way of implementing the ideal, via repre-
sentative government. The democratic ideal is more general than repre-
sentative government. The ideal says that everyone should have the

right to choose his/her own pattern of living, to say what they want, to choose jobs as they want, to move about as they want, to live with anyone they want, and so forth. Now in the two centuries of our experiment we have learned some lessons. We have learned, for example, that people often recognize democracy in the very narrow sense of applying only to people of their own kind, and the result is discrimination. We have also found that if you allow people to do what they want, they frequently do things that are harmful to others, including wildlife. That is, we have learned that "freedom" should go hand-in-hand with responsibility. Because the two are often not wedded, we have had to set up numerous government regulations so as to substitute collective responsibility for individual responsibility. But government regulations seems to be antithetical to the democratic ideal, and yet necessary to avoid anarchy.

I believe that the next century of our "test" of democracy will involve the critical examination of this question: how can we citizens of the U.S. bring together individual freedom and individual responsibility?

In the rest of this chapter I want to examine this question, using the U.S. Fish and Wildlife Service as a specific example.

I can begin by saying something more about "freedom." A free person is someone who desires certain things in his life, seeks ways of obtaining what he/she desires and makes real choices from a set of options to gain what he/she wants; he/she need not be "selfish," for the more desirable objective may be to help others. A free person, then, is one who lives without being deprived of the things in life that are most desired. We say that such a person behaves "teleologically," a word derived from the Greek word for purpose: "telos." Now to the scientist many objects in the world do not behave teleologically. Their behavior is best described by deterministic (or statistical) laws, as in the case with a rock falling off a cliff. We say that the rock follows "ateleological" laws.

The question I posed above can now be stated somewhat more precisely.

Suppose we compare two systems, the system we call a machine with the system we call a democratic organization. Both systems are

designed by humans to serve some set of purposes that humans deem
to be worthwhile; we say, therefore, that both systems are "teleological" and obey "teleological laws." Both systems are made up of components that somehow work together, well or badly, relative to the
desired objectives. But there is a critical difference. The parts of a
machine are *not* teleological, in the sense that they move in accordance
with deterministic laws. For example, a watch is a machine, its overall
purpose being to enable people to tell time. If it works with wheels,
then each wheel moves in accordance with some physical law. It does
not help our understanding of the way the wheels behave to say that
they "want to help," or "desire to coordinate with other cogs and
wheels." We can say this if we want to be cute about it, but if one of
the cogs or wheels fails to perform in accordance with some physical
law and the watch stops, it doesn't help to say that the cog or wheel
needs better motivation. The watch repairman will simply try to get
the cog or wheel back to moving in accordance with the physical law.
We say that machines are teleological wholes with ateleological parts.

Democratic organizations, on the other hand, are made up of people,
and people are "free," i.e., teleological; they want things, they are motivated, they change their purposes, and in general their behavior can be
explained by what they are trying to accomplish. We say that they act
in accordance with teleological laws. Organizations themselves are designed for certain overall purposes, to make a product, to teach young-
sters, or to protect wildlife. Democratic organizations, therefore, are
teleological wholes with teleological parts.

Now machines are usually much easier to manage than democratic
organizations, and this is the reason that many managers, past and present, have tried very hard to convert their organizations into machines.
They do this by setting forth some hard-and-fast rules. "I don't care
what you do with the rest of your life, but you must be here at 8 a.m.,
perform these activities, take this coffee and lunch break, and leave not
earlier than 5 p.m." Note that the rule sets up an ateleological set of
"laws," much like the laws that nature herself imposes on the cogs and
wheels of the watch. And if a worker fails to perform in accordance
with the rules, he is to be replaced by someone who will. But not always. Perhaps the personnel manager will talk to him and see if he can
change the aberrant worker's motivation. If so, the organization be-

comes less machine-like, perhaps.

We should also note that many models of organizations attempt to define the organization as a machine. This is certainly true of Forrester's "Dynamo" models and of linear programming. In both cases, the parts operate causally, i.e., in accordance with causal and not teleological laws.

If you really like what an organization is trying to accomplish, there is much to be said for trying to convert it into a machine. For one thing, it's usually much easier to fix it when it fails to function properly by getting its cogs and wheels back on the track, i.e., by getting them to obey the rules. Industrial factories are a good example. If you want to reduce costs, you can't afford to have people making up their minds as to what they'd like to do — knock off for a cup of coffee, or a bit of love-making — just when the process requires their attention.

Furthermore, if the aim is to serve people best, then a machine often seems the best way to do it. This is one reason why we have large government bureaucracies and so much government regulation; if procedures take place in accordance with hard and fast rules, then the citizens themselves benefit, so the argument goes.

I should add to the above, that the "laws" governing the machine need not be exactly deterministic: they may be proballistic instead. My favorite example is the case of the "suicide" system. The individual who has just jumped from the Golden Gate Bridge no doubt believes his jump to be the result of much deliberation and free choice, i.e., teleological; but an observing statistician may remark, "Yup, just fits in nicely into my frequency distribution." The statistician does not care about the myriad of tortuous pathways that have led people to commit suicide; the important point is that the probability of such action can be estimated with reasonable accuracy.

If we turn to the Fish and Wildlife Service, we can understand how tempting it is to regard the Service as a machine, and specifically as a machine that works in accordance with statistical laws. For the most part, one can predict within statistical limits the number of migratory birds of a given species that will land on a specific refuge, in October, say. That is, one can make such predictions if humans don't intervene. But humans, acting teleologically, like to develop industrial plants, to recreate, and generally to do things which disturb the statistical patterns of wildlife. To maintain the machine quality of the wildlife

system, the managers need to exclude humans from large regions, stop
certain development plans from being implemented, and prevent recreational activities like large motor boats on lakes where the migratory birds
land. Refuge managers like bird watchers because they tend to leave
the mechanical system as it is. Hunting is more difficult, but if regu-
lated (i.e., made more machine-like), it too need not disturb the smooth
workings of the system.

Now we can return to the question raised above and restate it as
follows: despite the fact that machine-like organizations tend to be
more efficient than democratic organizations with respect to overall goals,
how can we design a democratic organization whose members are "free"
(i.e., teleological) and at the same time the overall goals are attained?
Specifically, how can we design a Fish and Wildlife Service where the public are free in their choice of how refuges are to be used, and at the same
time the overall goal of preserving wildlife habitats is maintained?

One way to understand this question is to ask what steps should
be taken when something goes wrong, i.e., when the organization devi-
ates from its overall goal because some of its members become irrespons-
ible. Now machines also sometimes go wrong. The strategies of coping
with error in the case of machines seems fairly obvious: (1) we can design them better; (2) when they fail we can fix one or more parts; or
(3) replace one or more parts; or (4) throw the whole machine away.

In the case of organizations, these strategies become: (1) we can
plan better; (2) if some people thwart the organizational objectives we
can "fix them"; or (3) kill or otherwise remove them; or (4) disband
("kill") the organization. It's clear that managers of organizations often
try to use one of these machine-like strategies: (1) we try to plan better by foreseeing what people might do, and setting up rules to prevent
them from doing it (e.g., rules against hunting in "off seasons"); (2) we
try to persuade people to change their behavior through advertising, or
town meetings, workshops, or through threats of fines, etc.; or (3) we
imprison and sometimes kill offenders; and (4) we attempt to eliminate
some organizations altogether.

Here again the alienation of the manager from the people becomes
apparent. All these "machine strategies" seem basically inappropriate
if the ideal is to create democratic organizations rather than machines.

But what are alternative strategies to handle aberration in our society?

The most popular suggestion addresses the "we" in each case. How can we make the "we" include more people? The word for the attempt to do this is "participation." In some sense, the teleological parts of an organization need to become managers. They need to share not only in the planning, but also in the regulation of the organization. If people are to be motivated to change, or to be fined or imprisoned, or to give up an organization, the people need to share in deciding how each of these policies is to be framed and implemented.

But there is a paradox in the last paragraph that reveals itself in the second sentence: *we* are to broaden the "we." How is this broadening to occur? How shall the Wildlife Service involve more people in the planning, and regulation of its refuges, for example? *We* (the managers) will arrange town meetings preceded by advertisements and publications that will inform the public concerning the issues. *We* must be sure not to give the impression that *we* already have made up our minds.

It becomes obvious in this account that the social system which plans and regulates public participation is more like a machine than an organization: how participation is to take place is in the hands of the managers and not in the teleology of the public. This is one reason, I suspect, that members of organizations which try to implement participatory planning often turn cynical: they feel as though management were saying "participate, damn it, I said participate or else."

Of course, the key to the problem is the creation of responsibility on the part of the public. I said above that a democratic Fish and Wildlife Service would be one in which the public is free to choose how a refuge should be used. If the public has a high sense of responsibility, it will freely choose to use the refuge so as to protect wildlife habitats, just as the manager of the refuge does.

But what is the source of this responsibility on the part of the public? Now, whenever I become stuck with a question like this one, I turn to the past for some advice and discussion. In this case I've turned to Kant and Plato, and a more recent writer, Gerald Heard.

Kant was led by a rather tortuous argument to imagine a society in which everyone shares in the legislation, because each, out of his Good Will, acts in accordance with the same moral law. I say that Kant "imagines" this society, since it takes a strong imagination to appreciate it. The following gives some of this flavor of the image:

> By a *kingdom* I understand the union of different rational beings in a system of common laws — all rational beings come under the *law* that each must treat himself and all others never as *means only,* but in every case at the same time *as ends in themselves.* Hence results a systematic union of rational beings by common objective laws, i.e., a kingdom which may be called a kingdom of ends, since what these laws have in view is just the relation of these beings to one another as ends and means. It is certainly only an ideal. *(Foundations of the Metaphysics of Morals,* pp. (62-1.)

In another version of the same moral principle, Kant emphasizes that each of us must treat *humanity*, whether in our own person or in another, as an end, never as a means only. In amplifying on this idea, he remarks:

> It is not enough that the action does not violate humanity in our own person as an end in itself; it must also *harmonize* with it. Now humanity contains capacities for greater perfection, which belong to the end that nature has in view in regard to humanity: to neglect these might perhaps be consistent with the *maintenance* of humanity as an end in itself, but not with the *advancement* of this end. *(Foundations,* pp. 59-60)

Hence Kant's answer to the question posed above is that responsibility comes from the "moral law" that each of us holds potentially within him or herself. The origin of responsibility is morality, and morality is a part of every human soul.

Here is Plato in the *Phaedrus:* "Soul, considered collectively, has the care of all that which is soulless," i.e., the source of responsibility comes from the natural state of every human's caring for other living species.

My later writer is Gerald Heard in the *Social Substance of Religion* (1931). He tries to describe the essence of *community* through the triad "Love, Joy, Peace":

> The sudden discovery of a sense that others matter so much that I forget myself, this breaking out of Love, is the first step and must lead to an intense Joy . . . But as Love was a general self-forgetting ecstasy, so is its consequent Joy no quiet self-contented cheerfulness, but a

rapture that whoever experiences it knows he is pos-
sessed; body and spirit are no longer distinct, nor I
and you. This joy, however, because of its intensity,
cannot and ought not to last — Love leads to Joy,
and as inevitably as joy leads to peace." (pp. 222-3)

Hence the source of responsibility lies in the natural human inclination
towards forming community.

Heard thought that the truly religious community had the attributes just described, but that it was quite fragile, and if it grew, then
(as happened to Paul in his later years) rules and punishment take the
place of Love, and the religious spirit dies as the community becomes
transformed into a machine. He believed that the truly religious community needs to be small.

I'm not sure I agree with him, or at least I hope he is wrong, because I want to say that true "public participation" means something
like Kant's kingdom of ends, or Plato's caring, or Heard's religious
community.

The word "partake" has the same roots as "participation," and to
participate in planning and decision making should mean partaking of
the life of the organization. In the case of the Fish and Wildlife Service
it means that we create a public which legislates equally about wildlife
(Kant), cares as much as the refuge directors about the welfare of wildlife (Plato), and shares a non-ego involvement in the love, joy and peace
of its relationship with wildlife (Heard). True participation does *not*
mean having a vote on the regulations, sharing in the decision to close
or open a wilderness area, or the fines to be imposed on illegitimate
hunting. These are shadows of participation, somewhat meaningless if
true participation is not there. Participation means freedom with responsibility rooted in morality, sharing and community spirit.

I'm not saying that we can avoid some group's initiating the first
steps of true participation. I think someone has to start the rudiments
of public community built around a spiritual feeling about humanity's
relation to other living beings.

But I am saying that the "measure of performance" of such first
steps can be considered in terms of a reduction in the need for regulation. I believe we who appreciate the grand experiment of democracy
find that there is far too much government regulation, but the answer
is *not* to reduce regulation. Indeed, often those who criticize government

regulations are on the side of the greedy, who kill community in Heard's sense whenever they can. Government regulation is a symptom of some- thing wrong, not a cause. The cause is that we have not yet learned how to create the communal, unselfish democracy that will make regu- lations superfluous.

I'm not sure how the first steps should be made. I don't think they can be made by calling people into a series of hearings or even workshops. Of course, we must emphasize to the public that "it's your Wildlife Service," not ours. And that the kind of Service they should have is to be designed around their goals, and not just Congress's or the executive branch's.

So my "public participation" question might be posed as follows. Select some Service Regulations as a beginning, and ask "what might the Service do to make these regulations superfluous?"

I'd like to close with three practical suggestions that might begin to design the pathway to true public participation in the Wildlife Service.

The first is quite mundane. Replace all "Public Prohibited" signs with ones reading "This is Your Wildlife Refuge! To Preserve the Birds and Animals, Please Do Not Enter This Area." It takes longer to say, but the message is better.

Second, let's not confine public participation to specific issues. For example, on selected refuges near towns, hold "Refuge Picnics," at which experts and non-experts talk and share views about the function and performance of the Service.

Third, form regional wildlife clubs (associations) where people can share in the Service's functions.

Now I realize that a number of people, perhaps most in the en- forcement end of the Service's business, will find this chapter naive in the extreme, because they have learned, the hard way, that people are out for themselves. They believe that, given a polite sign like the one above, with its "please" and absence of threat, people will be even more inclined to enter the area and shoot what they find.

We are back to an age-old dilemma about the basics of humans. I've selected three authors, Plato, Kant and Heard, all of whom believed people are basically good. But I could have selected another three, Machia- velli, Hobbes and Hume, say, who believed, not that people are bad necessarily, but that they seek to maximize their own power or pleasure.

It is true that each of the sources of responsibility given above, morality, sharing and community, may well turn sour. Morality is often the producer of bigotry; bigotry is the disease of morality. For example, bigotry might say that children should be forbidden to enter a refuge because they are too young to sense the importance of wildlife. Similarly, "sharing with the soulless" may well produce a feeling of superiority which leads to the belief that because wildlife are dumb and inferior to humans, we can do unto them as we please, including killing off a whole species such as the coyote. Superiority is the disease of sharing with the soulless. And finally, a sense of community may produce what I call "blind politics," people gathering together around one answer to an issue, e.g., the answer of opening up a refuge for public recreation and blocking out any information that runs counter to their beliefs. Blind politics is the disease of community feeling.

Hence I conclude that the Fish and Wildlife Service should be in the business of public health, i.e., of preventing and curing the diseases of democratic society.

10

AN APPRECIATION OF
EDGAR ARTHUR SINGER, JR.

I have selected the title of this chapter rather carefully. An appreciation of someone's lifetime work is not just an evaluation; it is also a process of adding to and adjusting the results of that lifetime of creation of ideas and a system of philosophy. As Singer would put it, an appreciation "sweeps in" new ideas and corrections for the system.

As some of this paper is technical and not easy to follow, I shall begin by a fairly brief summary of what I intend to discuss. In the beginning, is a mystery. Why is it that Singer's work in the theory of knowledge (epistemology) was and still is largely ignored by professional philosophers? It is correct to say that Singer is far better known today by students of social systems science than he is known by students in philosophy courses. Why? Because, I think, Singer adopted a completely radical point of view in his philosophy of science, namely, the complete rejection of simplicity in matters of fact: there are no simple facts of nature known by us "directly". According to Singer, if a person sets

* Given 12 September 1981 as the First Edgar Arthur Singer, Jr., Lecture of the Busch Center at Wharton School, University of Pennsylvania. This paper was completed in April 1982.

out to answer any question of fact, he finds that he must learn more
and more about the world, i.e., he discovers that his original question
becomes more and more complicated, *not* simpler and simpler. This
"learning more and more" is what, following Singer, I call the "sweep-in
process" of systems science. Practically all of Singer's contemporaries in
philosophy believed so thoroughly in a hierarchy of simplicity, ranging
from the deeply complex to the purely simple, that they lacked the ears
to hear Singer's message. Those of us who practice social systems science
learn the hard way that there are no simple questions and that the process
of addressing a specific question will eventually require answers to more
and more questions, i.e., require the "sweep-in" process.

In order to explain Singer's approach, I need to become somewhat
technical for a while because his approach was based on a statistical
theory, namely, the Theory of Least Squares, or what today we would
call "analysis of variance", which is basic to the understanding of human
knowledge.

It seems to have been Gauss, around 1800, who "discovered" the
theory of least squares as he became curious as to the best way to fit a
straight line to a set of observed points. His mathematical intuition
told him that one should want to minimize some function of the deviations of the points from the fitted line. In other words, there are many
choices (actually an infinity of them) of straight lines that in some sense
fit the points, and one should use as a criterion the line that minimizes
some function of the deviations. The function Gauss chose was the sum
of the squares of the deviations. Why? There seems to be both an economic and a mathematical response to this question. The economic response says that the deviations of the points from the line are "errors"
in the sense that in all likelihood no line fits the points perfectly. For
Gauss, the economic cost of error should not be assumed to be linear
in the size of the error because small errors are not nearly so important
as larger ones for those who want to use the fitted line for some practical purpose. The squares would reflect this economic assumption: a
deviation of 0.5 costs in proportion to $(0.5)^2 = 0.25$, whereas a deviation
of 10 costs in proportion to $10^2 = 100$. The mathematical reason for
choosing the sum of squares to minimize is that quadratic functions of
this type are far simpler to handle than, say, the absolute values of the
deviations.

From Gauss's important discovery, some important epistemological principles follow. First, if one is given a set of observed quantities that pertain to a fact of nature (e.g., the distance between two points on the surface of the earth at a moment in time), then the "best" estimate of the true (but unknown) fact is the sample mean because the sample mean (sum of the given quantities of observation divided by the number of them) minimizes the sum of the squared deviations. Second, one also needs to estimate the error of this "best" estimate if the estimate is to be used for some practical purpose (e.g., fixing the boundaries of building lots). The best estimate of the error is again some function of the squared deviations; the average sum of the squared deviations, slightly modified, is called the "sample variance;" and its square root, the sample standard deviation. The second epistemological principle, for Singer, is that any response to a question of fact has merit only when an estimate of the error of the estimate is given or, as we would say today, only when a confidence interval is supplied.

It should be noted that I have used the phrase "has merit only", rather than "has meaning only", because Singer's theory of epistemology is based on the pragmatic value (merit), rather than the much weaker notion of semantic meaning. Meritorious estimates require some additional estimates about how reliable they are, whereas in a lot of our discourse, we skip error estimations because although we are conversing in a meaningful way, the merit of our remarks is minimal.

Third, it is essential to know how the observations are made or, to use the language of statistical theory, how an item is drawn from a population. This epistemological postulate is so central to Singer's thought and so different from the thought processes of his contemporaries that it no doubt accounts for the fact that his contemporaries largely ignored his work. I have elsewhere argued that problem statements are gateways into the complexities of a system, but I now need to add that not all such gateways lead to enlightenment. To state the wrong problem may lead one into a labyrinth of deception. To me, this is exactly what happened to John Locke in the seventeenth century: he stated the wrong epistemological problem and led himself and all his followers up to the present day, including the logical positivists, into the philosophical labyrinth called empiricism. Locke's question was "Which sensations are the simplest in that they reveal the true fact directly?" He also asked a subsidiary question, "What can be induced from the directly known sensations?" Once a person believes that epistemology must start with these two problems, he will never find the nature of the whole system of knowledge because the gateway leads to pathways that circle back and around in the manner of a labyrinth, sometimes leading him to believe he has a new insight because he has entered a new corridor where he has never been before, only to find that it too leads back to the same old scepticism about induction.

One example should suffice: Suppose for the moment that the sensation of white is a plausible candidate for Locke's first question: one might say that sensation is "simple" (because it cannot be analyzed further) and reveals a true fact about an object directly. Suppose the inductive generalization is "all swans are white". Then an empiricist mind, caught in Locke's labyrinth, might travel about in first-class hotels in the U.S.A. and U.K., delighted to find its generalization confirmed over and over. It might even use Carnap's degree of confirmation of an hypothesis and smugly watch the degree approaching certainty. Then one day, it takes a trip to Japan's International Hotel in Kyoto and sadly watches the black swans as they swim around in the pond there. It might suspect that the clever and artistic Japanese had dyed them all black; but later it goes to New Zealand, where black swans abound, and realizes that the frugal New Zealanders would never put up the funds to dye all of the swans black.

Singer's third point is that unless a person can confirm that his observations were drawn correctly from the population of swans, he cannot have any confidence whatsoever in his induction. The fact that the sensation of white seems simple and direct to the observer contributes nothing to the epistemological status of "all swans are white". Furthermore, in the halcyon days of his earlier journeys, he never once asked, "What is the error in my judgment that *this* swan is white?" He never asked this question because he believed in direct, nonanalyzable sensations. Had he escaped from Locke's labyrinth, he would have understood that "whiteness" lay on some continuum of degrees of whiteness and he would have made estimates of the degree for any swan, plus or minus an error term. Thus the stipulation that the mode of observation is a crucial element in any epistemology means that one must make the observations in a manner that guarantees that they are drawn from the population correctly and that a set of observations can be used to estimate the mean and the confidence interval.

The first three stipulations of a sound epistemology were captured beautifully in an article by Henry Bradford Smith in 1928 in the *Journal of Philosophy.* The title of it was "Postulates of Empirical Thought." His first postulate reads: "There is nothing to be found in the meaning of experience that is not already contained in the meaning of experiment."

One can recognize the aesthetic arrogance that Smith shared with Singer regarding their philosophical convictions by the fact that Smith called this statement a "postulate", thereby suggesting to his contemporaries that it be given the status of being self-evident.* Smith, as well as Singer, must have known that practically all their contemporaries believed in the existence of a class of direct and simple observations and that "direct observation" had none of the characteristics of an experiment, though Smith in the article never once suggested this fact. An experiment requires a careful calibration of instruments, a very careful method of random selection of items from a population, a method of measurement on one or more scales, and so on. No experimenter steeped in the problems of designing a good experiment could possibly say that his results were obtained "directly." One is reminded of Ambrose Bierce's definition of "self-evident": evident to one's self and one's self only. I think that both Smith and Singer believed that once you had explained matters to misguided philosophers, they would "come around".

There is no better example of Singer's teacher-student relationship to his contemporaries than his handling of the philosophical speculation called "solipsism", which says that I have no way of knowing whether you or anyone else is "conscious" the way I am because I can experience only my own feelings and sensations. For all I know, says the argument, the whole world of humanity may be unconscious machines, even though each person behaves much as I do. The following passage is from one of his earlier works. It is directed to those philosophers who think they have successfully handled solipsism.

---

*   I am aware of the fact that both Singer and Smith used "postulate" in its etymological sense of a "demand" or even "request", but they surely needed to explain the rational source of the demand.

MIND AS AN OBSERVABLE OBJECT [32]

It is seldom given to philosophers to enter into one another's enthusiasms, but they are sometimes allowed to share a disappointment. And could anything be more generally disappointing than the attitude of a certain important group of natural philosophers toward the study of minds? I refer to that curious bit of reasoning commonly known as the "analogy argument" which runs somehow thus: I am aware, and I alone am aware, that certain of my bodily acts are accompanied by mental states. When I observe similar acts in other bodies I infer that they too are accompanied by like states of mind. No experience can be brought to confirm this inference, but then nothing can transpire to refute it. Meanwhile, my feelings are spared a severe strain by risking it — the loneliness of not risking it is too tragic to be faced.

The objectionable points of this line of argument are just all the points of its make-up. To begin with, it is so far from self-evident that each man's mental state is his own indisputable possession, no one hesitates to confess at times that his neighbor has read him better than he has read himself, nor at other times to claim that he knows his neighbor's state of mind more truly than the neighbor himself knows it. No one finds fault with Thackeray for intimating that the old Major is a better judge of Pendennis's feeling for the Fotheringay than is Pendennis himself. To be sure, we are more likely to accept such situations when the state of mind read from the outside is complex and subtle; but there should be no difference in principle between the diagnosis of love and a test for color-blindness. It is quite as likely that under certain conditions I do not know what red is, as that under other conditions I do not know what love is. In a word, so long as we are social beings our judgments, even the simplest of them, have social meanings, and each knows himself through others.

Next, the analogy argument calls its procedure an inference. Now, everybody knows an inference from a thousand cases to be more valuable than one drawn from a hundred, an anticipation based on a hundred observations to be safer than one with only ten to support it. But there are those who, knowing all this, would conclude that an inference from one instance has *some* value. If in my case mental states accompany my body's behavior, there is at least *some* ground for supposing like acts of another's body to be in like manner paralleled. This illusion, for it is one, springs I think from a failure to catch the meaning of inference. An inference from a single case, if it be really an inference from a single case, has exactly no value at all. No one would be tempted to attribute eight planets to every sun because our sun has eight such satellites. The

---

32.   From *Mind as Behavior,* first published in 1924 and recently republished by the AMS Press, New York (1981).

reason a single observation is sometimes correctly assumed to have weight is that the method of observing has been previously tested in a variety of cases. The shop-keeper measures his bit of fabric but once; he has however measured other fabrics by the same method numberless times, and has a fairly clear idea of the probable error of his result. But the principle holds absolutely of all results: no series of observations, no probable error; no ground for inference; no meaning as a datum.

Nor is our line of argument happier in its next point. The hypothesis of other minds is one that must be regarded as referring to the *Jenseits* of things that make a difference to my experience. There is a fair definition of pragmatism to be found among the last sayings of the man whose absence this day leaves us lonely indeed; a definition tempting me to think I have always been, in all innocence, a pragmatist:

"The serious meaning of a concept," writes James, following Peirce, "lies in the concrete difference to someone which its being true will make. Strive to bring all debated conceptions to that "pragmatic" test, and you will escape vain wrangling . . . If it can make no practical difference whether a given statement be true or false, then the statement has no real meaning."[33]

If the method defined in this passage be accepted, and I cannot see how any one can fail to accept it even if one prove unfaithful to it afterwards, then could anything more fully illustrate the meaning of the "meaningless" than that hypothesis of other minds in which the analogy argument culminates? Whatever may be said for the reasoning, is its conclusion at least right? Alas, I cannot know. If right, my experience cannot inform me; if wrong, my experience cannot disillusion me. It makes no practical difference to me whether I am right or wrong. Pragmatic conclusion: I cannot have made a meaningful hypothesis.

The passage was a favorite among Singer's students, not so much because it slew the enemies, but because it reduced them to philosophical children, the innocents in the literal sense of those who knew nothing. The teacher had returned their term papers with the remark that every one of their premises was wrong.

Perhaps I can portray the magnitude of Singer's break with traditional philosophy in another manner. Locke's way of stating the basic epistemological problem seems eminently reasonable: We need, he said, to start with what we can safely say we know and then proceed to see how we can use what we know to acquire knowledge about what we do

---

33. *Meaning of Truth,* p. 52.

not know. On the contrary, had Smith stated *his* postulate in this kind of language, he would have said: In the design of inquiry, start with what you don't know. I wonder if he would have dared to label this prescription a "postulate" if he had stated it that way. His own version says much the same thing, however, as anyone who has ever tried to design a good experiment will recognize. In experimental design, we start with what we do not know: we do not know that the sample has been drawn properly (What is a "random" sample?); we do not know that the instruments are calibrated; we do not know that all relevant variables have been included; and so on.

Of course, Smith's prescription did not tell us to start with total ignorance; it said to start with the difficult and not the simple, the difficult task being to design an experiment rather than to observe a color or hear a sound.

Now, I'd like to make an adjustment of one of Singer's contributions. My conversation up to this point has been about the epistemology of questions of fact, and its topic has been dealing with how we address questions of fact. But as Singer told us, at the time of Locke there was another theory of simplicity, namely, the simplicities of reason. This time it was Spinoza who posed the question most clearly. Spinoza asked which propositions of pure reason were the simplest and were known directly. Singer made Locke's question and Spinoza's question the beginning of what he called the "dialectic of the schools," with Kant as the great synthesizer. [34]

I think we students looked on the dialectic in a vastly oversimplified way by regarding Locke as the thesis and Spinoza as the antithesis, and we regarded these as on the same "level" because they were both asking about simplicities, the simplicities of fact and law (theory). I now believe Singer's dialectic of the schools needs adjustment. In the first place, I believe that the antithesis in a well-designed dialectical process is not just a logical contrary of the thesis; it is usually more subtle, more challenging, more difficult to comprehend, and yet more comprehensive. It moves the dialectical process. Hence, I believe

---

34. Singer, Edgar Arthur, Jr., *Experience and Reflection,* ed. by C. West Churchman. Philadelphia: University of Pennsylvania Press, 1959.

Spinoza's question is different in kind from Locke's. Rationalists like
Spinoza sensed the eternal verity of the elementary propositions of logic,
arthmetic, and geometry. The manner in which $2 + 2 = 4$ can be understood as a very complicated assertion is far more subtle than the manner
in which "this is white" can be understood to be complicated. But going
into this matter of rationalism in any depth would take me far beyond
the bonds of this chapter.

In my own lifetime, I have found that Singer's and Smith's philosop-
ical advice has had a tremendous influence on everything that I have tried
to do on a professional level. When I first left the ivory tower, I worked
for a U.S. Army Ordnance Laboratory. One of my tasks was to redesign
the method of testing small-arms ammunition for misfires. The method in
use when I joined the laboratory consisted of starting with the simple procedure of testing the primers at an energy level where one expected that
all of them would go off if they were correctly manufactured. It is a
simple matter to find out if a primer does go off because it makes a fairly
loud "bang", loud enough to warm the cockles of a Lockean heart. The
testing method said that if a hundred went off in a row, one could induce
that all in the lot would go off at that energy and that the soldier in the
field should have no fear of misfires. But, bearing Smith's advice in
mind, I asked myself how good the experiment actually was; and the
answer I got was that it was not very good at all. Could one safely induce 100% firing from a sequence of one hundred firings? The answer
came directly out of probability theory. Suppose that, in fact, there were
1% misfires in the lot: What would be the probability of not hearing a
misfire in the first one hundred tested? The answer is about 1/3; so,
as a consequence, very bad lots could pass the test quite frequently.

So, being cognizant that I was not really interested in whether a
primer fired at a given energy, I addressed the difficult question: What
I would really like to know about any primer would be its critical energy, the energy below which it would not fire and above which it would,
because then, knowing the energy delivered by the firing pin in a gun, I
would be able to predict the performance of the lot in the field. But
for any individual primer, there is no way to obtain the measure of the
critical energy because once you hit the primer, it no longer belongs to
the same species wherein it started, whether or not it fires. By exploring

in the energy region where some go off and some do not, however, one can use probability theory to derive the distribution of critical energies and thereby infer from that probability distribution the energy required to detonate almost all of the primers in a lot. If this energy is less than the energy delivered by a firing pin in a gun, one can be almost sure of success in the field. Thus, what could not be known about any single item just because it went off could be known about a collection of items; and addressing the difficult question enabled us to do something that addressing the so-called simple question could not, namely, to assure the firing quality of the product.

This is not the end of the matter, of course. The whole procedure may be faulty because the assumptions that were made in testing the primers may have been wrong. So I come to the heart of Singer's philosophy of inquiry, the "sweep-in process". All of Singer's students believed that the problems we humans face are closely interconnected so that the only way we can study a system is to recognize the need to be comprehensive. But this prescription seems to be either paradoxical or hopelessly impractical. Recently I was watching a TV program on prisons in the U.S.A., where the possibility of another Attica was the main topic of conversation. At first, the problem was posed as one of reducing overcrowding in the prisons and eliminating bad food. To pose *the* problem in this manner is to believe that *the* problem of our society with regard to those who break the law is how to put them someplace where they will not harm others or themselves, much as, for many people today, *the* problem of the elderly is how to get them out of sight. But from a systems point of view, *the* problem is not prisons at all, but rather what makes people commit crimes. This second way of stating the problem opens up the inquiry and expands the boundaries of the system.

Any wary student of systems science immediately sniffs danger when the professor talks in this manner. He, the student, has to write a term paper or a thesis; and if he chooses to write it on prison reform, he can readily sense that his chances of completing his task in any prescribed time period are minimal. The professor has just cracked the barriers of the prison system and pushed the student unwillingly into the larger social world of "causes of crime". Even a very naive student would be aware that in a society like the U.S.A., unemployment is surely

one of the chief "causes" of crime. So now, dear student, why don't
you study the employment system and ask why an affluent society like
ours allows an unemployment rate of seven or more percent? This question will take you to at least two other systems, government and private
enterprise. Naturally, the student cries out, "Professor, tell me how to
bound the system!"

The professor's reply might well be, "It doesn't matter because
you are not going to *solve* the problem of prison reform. No real problem is ever solved once and for all. The problems of human society are
not like exercises at the end of a chapter of a textbook, where all the
information is given for you to deduce a perfect answer. But you can
make some progress if you can begin to 'sweep-in' to your inquiry
the broader issues."

Suppose we consider how Singer used to explain the professor's
reply to his class of graduate students at the University of Pennsylvania
in the first year of his three-year sequence of courses on what he called
the analysis of concepts. He began, not with an issue so apparently
difficult as prison reform, but rather with a very practical, down-to-
earth matter such as "What is the distance between two points, A and
B, on the surface of the earth at a specific moment of time, t?" Suppose this question is an important, practical one for a person who is
owner of a piece of land because he needs a reply to it in order to use
the information to decide where to build his house. In all likelihood,
he will hire a surveyor to determine the distance. The surveyor will set
up his instruments; and, if he knows his business, he will make several
determinations from which he will calculate the average and standard
deviation, and hence a confidence interval.

It is important to notice that in addressing the question of fact of
the distance, the inquiring system has made a lot of fairly complicated
theoretical and factual assumptions: arithmetical, geometrical, and opti-
cal, for example. A cautious empiricist might want to check each assumption by reducing it to its simplest elements and testing the veracity
of these. We can now understand that the discussion at the beginning
of this chapter was a discussion about the strategies of inquiry, the design of inquiring systems. Which is better, to reduce the system to its
elements or to expand the system? A system-science reply would be that

since there are no simple, elementary questions, the first strategy is based on illusion and the second is the one to be followed.

Having gotten the surveyor's report, the owner might feel that it would end the inquiry into the distance AB as far as he was concerned; but his next-door neighbor might dispute the finding, saying that the owner was planning to build his house too close to the neighbor's property line. Now a second surveyor is hired, and his results differ radically from those of the first. What "differ radically" really means is partially a statistical matter. Statistical theory provides ways of determining whether the two are radically different. This brings us to the question of the strategy for the case of statistically incompatible results. The strategy has to be one of "sweeping-in" more of the system, of explaining how it happened that two observers, in this case two surveyors, arrived at radically different results.

In Singer's seminar, he illustrated the "sweep-in" process by an example from Bessel's *Observations of Planetary Motion in the Heavens.* Bessel found that different observers made observations that differ significantly from the observations of other observers. He came to the conclusion that as observers watch a body passing through the telescope, some observers are the over-anxious types who want to make sure that they get the planet at the right time. They tend to respond too quickly and record the observation before the center of the body gets to the hairline. Others tend to want to be very safe and wait until they are sure: they tend to record the observation after the body has passed the hairline. Bessel's experience led to a whole theory of response time in psychology, a theory which would have to be "swept in" to the observing system. The question of fact has necessitated bringing in psychological theory.

When I was at the Frankfort Arsenal during World War II, I did a lot of this kind of work. Most of what I did at the Arsenal was calibration work.

It happened that almost every measurement process I studied during World War II was out of statistical control; the measurement processes were not calibrated properly. For example, the metallurgists in the laboratory were worried about the accuracy of their metallurgical measurements. We took a steel bar and indented it in the Rockwell hardness manner by dropping a little diamond on the surface of the steel bar. The result was a small diamond-shaped indentation on the surface. The observer then had to line up the hairline in his microscope at one vertex of that indentation, roll the hairline over to the other end and then record the distance that the roll entailed. He then repeated this process several times.

We sent that steel bar to twenty laboratories and asked them to have two or more observers in each laboratory determine the Rockwell hardness by doing what I have just described. Each laboratory had two to about ten observers go through the procedure. When we had received all the results, we found that many of the laboratories were statistically consistent but that there was one laboratory that reported a Rockwell hardness harder than that of any known steel, and another laboratory that reported a Rockwell hardness about the hardness of lead. Why? We found that there was consistency among observers in the same lab. In other words, a standard analysis of variance revealed no significant difference among the independent observations made by observers in the same lab, but there was a significant difference among laboratories. These findings suggested to us that each laboratory had its own culture, probably created by someone who trained all the other observers. Hence, we had to "sweep in" a sociological or cultural anthropological theory.

Many of you, I am sure, have gone through the experience of having blood tests which are performed by some laboratory. The results are reported to your physician, who may tell you, "This is rather a serious matter," or "You're OK." You will be interested to know that medical laboratories suffer from the same problems as do metallurgical laboratories. That's my comfort for the day!

During the War, I visited fifteen different laboratories in order properly to calibrate the measurement of the sensitivity of small-arms primers. I used to worry so much about calibration that I made a nuisance of myself. I would ask one of my physicist friends, "How dare you conduct your experiments in the sloppy way you do when your measurements are not calibrated?" For example, Birge, at the University of California, Berkeley, discovered that the measurement of physical constants by independent observers were all statistically out of control. Russ Ackoff and I at one time became interested in the various determinations of the velocity of white light in a vacuum and found that they were all statistically out of control. So here is a science, physics, calling itself an "exact" science and yet having measurements out of control.

For many of us, however, the "sweep-in" process, as Singer used it, seemed rather slow and modest. A bit of psychology was "swept in" here or a bit of social psychology there in order to calibrate instruments and adjust observations. Furthermore, Singer (and I in World War II) lived in a pre-computer age. Computers can be programmed to correct a lot of the mistakes in the measurement process. But this development hardly avoids the necessity of "sweeping in" because now the theory that needs to be "swept in" is computer science. In computer-science software, the calibration process is called "documentation", and until recently it has been in very bad shape.

Now, I would like to turn to social systems design, the effort to improve social systems through planning.

I have already suggested how "sweep-in" works in this area, namely, where we find that a system like a prison or a hospital is in difficulty. The planner should search not for ways to make the prison or the hospital run more smoothly, but for the reasons why we have things like badly run prisons and hospitals. The reasons turn out to be political, as much as economic; hence, the planner needs to "sweep in" the causes of the existence of the troubled organization, and these causes lie in other systems.

Another example of a somewhat different kind is the food system of the world. There is no doubt in my mind and the minds of my colleagues at Berkeley that the food system of the world is in terribly bad shape. We estimate that as many as one billion people are now seriously malnourished because of lack of an adequate food supply. The reason why we have a food system is obvious. The mystery is why in a world of humanity which has enough food to feed everyone, we have allowed such mass inhuman starvation, especially if we assume that most humans are both intelligent and compassionate.

For a long while, the U.N. and the affluent nations assumed that since people are starving, the rest of the world should feed them. This simplistic solution led to a plethora of food programs, almost all of which failed. One way to put the situation is this: If you compare the world food system today in 1981 with the food system shortly after World War II, ours today is worse. One reason is that the world population has increased; but even if we take population increase into account, the food situation is still deteriorating. One of the reasons is that as food programs went into effect, the natives of each village began to rely on the food program and lost the knack and interest in supplying themselves with food. India has one of the most severe problems of malnutrition today, but has had a surplus of grain in the last two years. Why? The Indian food system has to be understood not just in terms of its own supply and demand, but in terms of the political and economic system of that country and the world.

Now, I want to do some adjusting of Singer's "sweep-in" process. Both of the examples I have given you are good, and he would have recognized them without any trouble; but in systems planning there is a very general "sweep-in" process which applies to all problem areas and establishes the strong interconnection of all social problems. I can illustrate what I mean by one of the early studies we conducted for the Warner-Swasey Company in Cleveland, Ohio. The Warner-Swasey Company manufacturers large road-building and road-repairing equipment. The managers believed they held a much larger inventory than was appropriate. The problem was to determine what the word "appropriate" meant. Most of the effort of operations researchers in the area of inventory has been designing more and more complicated mathematical models, whereas we found that our greatest difficulty was in obtaining the right data. In the theory of inventory control, one tries to balance as best one can two basic costs, the cost of ordering too much and having too large an inventory and the cost of ordering too little and having to reorder or to restart the machines or to face shortages. So what are these costs? Well, a little common sense and a little literature search showed us that the cost of holding inventory could be measured in terms of possible obsolescence, possible deterioration, but, most important, the cost of tied-up capital. What does it cost to tie up a hundred thousand dollars in inventory?

I would like to break away from inventory for the moment in order to introduce an awesome philosophical speculation which arises from this question. The verb "to decide" comes from the Latin word "to cut", or, rather, "to cut off". Once a person decides to do A, he decides *not* to do a plethora of other things. He "cuts off" a myriad of other lives he could have had just as effectively as the headsman cuts off a head to end a life. So my cheerful speculation is that we spend our decision-making lives murdering all kinds of lives, the lives we cut off by our decisions.

But back to the practical: How are we going to estimate the opportunity cost of holding inventory of a hundred thousand dollars for several months? How do we reason about such a question? What most of the textbooks in operations research suggest is consideration of what other investments there would be for that money. The authors argue that the hundred thousand dollars could be in the money market, for example, at p% interest; so the cost is p% per annum. If that is the answer, the conclusion might be that the whole company should be put into the money market! Why doesn't it just sell them all and put the resulting money into the money market? For many companies, this might be the right answer, of course; but the question is not how the company uses a hundred thousand dollars, but how it *should* use it. That's the "sweep-in" question, which goes immediately out of inventory into the cash-flow system and, indeed, into the whole financial investment system of the company. So, the problem is *not* inventory, but the financial operation of the company.

The problem of prison reform is *not* a problem of prisons. The problem of food shortage is *not* a problem of food. The same thing applies for data on the demand for inventory. Again, operations-research textbooks foolishly tell the poor students, "Go into the files and find out how much has been sold previously!" They are "poor" students because when they get out into the world, they will find that, for one thing, companies do not keep their records that way. For another, even if the companies did, would the past be relevant? Past records would tell only how much the demand had been. As practicing operations researchers, they ought to be interested in not what demand was in the past but in what demand should be, a point that has been well recognized by the telephone company and harvester companies, who adjust their demand by pricing.

So that's where our reasoning led us. And how are we going to "sweep-in" all these connected systems? Who can help us? Who knows about costs? Cost accounting? Where else would we expect to go but to the cost-accounting department to ask it, "What is the cost of holding a hundred thousand dollars in inventory?" But in the cost-accounting textbooks at that time, no one even mentioned opportunity costs.

Russ and I had a bright idea: We would tell the accounting profession what we had discovered, that opportunity costing is much the most important item of cost of any that a firm faces. We wrote an article and sent it off to the *Journal of Accountancy:* we called it "Operational Accounting." I think we had one request for a reprint! Conclusion: Cost accounting is not about real, practical costs.

Singer was perfectly right: There is the necessity for "sweep-in" but opportunity costing, opportunity demand, and so on, constitute the "sweep-in" principle that is the basis of it all. To repeat what I said earlier, the salient issue is not how much the inventory costs or how much the manager thinks it costs, but how much it *should* cost. The "should" is ethical.

Now I go back to the beginning of the chapter and say this about Singer's method: The basic epistemological problem is not to be posed as what is the distance between A and B on the surface of the earth at a moment of time, but whether I should be investigating that problem at all. That is not a question of science, per se; so the implication of Singer's "sweep-in"-process philosophy is that there is no such thing as the philosophy of science, per se, that all issues we try to investigate are based on a systems approach in which we have to ask, "Is the investigation warranted ethically?"

Hence, ethics is the basis of all epistemology; and ethics in its questioning is far broader than just inquiry. That's why Singer, for example, differs so radically from Popper, because Popper sees the problem as essentially an epistemological one, whereas the implication of Singer's philosophy is that the problem of a question of fact is an ethical one: "Should such a question be investigated?"

It may be helpful to make one more philosophical digression, and that is to speculate about the role of history in planning. If history means an estimate of what happened in the past, history may or may not be relevant. When the authors of *Limits to Growth* prepared their world model, they used the history of the past seven decades of the management of the world in relation to such matters as population, industrial production, and other factors. Their investigation tried to tell us what man's future would be like if the world would be managed in the future as it had been in the past. Hence, history played a crucial role in their determination that within two centuries there would occur a tremendous disaster. Such a use of history may be quite appropriate; but the historical accounts of how a company has used its liquidity or sold its products may not be relevant at all because the company may have mismanaged both. Similarly, if we ask how the world of the future should be managed, the problem of the proper role of history in our investigations may become extremely complicated.

The notion that the good should precede the true in man's inquiry takes me at the end to Singer's ethics, and to me it is a matter of much interest and concern. Singer did have an ethics that he wrote primarily towards the end of his life. It appears in two books, *On the Contented Life* (1936) and *In Search of a Way of Life* (1948). His was an ideal philosophy of ethics, that is, ethics is to be discussed in the context of human ideals. Singer saw, however, that there was a dialectic between the realists and the idealists. The realist is a down-to-earth, practical person who tries to solve the practical, hard problems of every-day life in a practical, coherent fashion. The realist goes to management-development programs and expects to find out what to do next Monday to become a better realist. The idealist tries to understand the human saga in terms of human ideals and their meaning in the very long run, and he sees that there is a constant struggle towards an ideal society. He tries as best he can to explain what that ideal might be, an ideal health service, an ideal university, an ideal whatever, and then to find out what is blocking us from the ideal and how we can get the roadblocks out of the way. Both philosophies occur in operations research. The realist regards himself as a problem-solver: he goes out and looks at inventory problems or at transportation problems or at whatever problem is under consideration. The idealist does his best to see, not just what particular problems a manager wants to solve, but what the ideal system might be and what prevents our getting there.

Singer tried his hand at doing the latter for the whole of humanity; and he came up with four ideals, the first three of which pretty much represent what we would call "development" today. He attempted, first, to create a better society economically in terms of resources and, second, to create education among those who would live in that society so that they would know how to use their resources in sensible ways. The third aspect that he recognized, which we do not normally throw into development because our nation is dominated by economics, he called "cooperation". From the point of view of the ideal of world cooperation, the United States of America is a very underdeveloped nation. It does not know at all how to handle the problem of national and international cooperation. Instead, it finds more and more dangerous means of increasing the degree of noncooperation. So, from Singer's point of view, we would have to say today that it is highly questionable whether the United States or the U.S.S.R. or any of the so-called affluent nations are "developed".

But it is Singer's fourth ideal that I want to discuss in concluding this chapter. If he were living today, he would have been shocked by the universal use of the word "satisfied". It seems to imply that all we are anxious to do is get ourselves to the level of being satisfied. That's not what humanity is like from Singer's point of view. He thought that psychologically we as humans were all dissatisfied, or should be, and that the feeling did not have to be negative at all. It just had to be human. It is not all pleasant either: if a person is dissatisfied, he is not finding an aura of pleasantness. But most of us are strugglers!

Since Singer's day, the richness of the idea of dissatisfaction has been explored for me most deeply in depth psychology, especially by Jung. At one time, towards the end of Singer's life, I thought he ought to read Jung; and I still have in my file the letter from Singer saying, "I have been trying to do what you told me to do, read Jung; but I find it so difficult." It was not really necessary that Singer read Jung: it was up to the rest of us to adjust Jung to the Singerian system or vice versa. There is a quotation from Jung that runs somewhat as follows: "We all say that we want to avoid trouble and we all say we look forward to removing it once and for all; and yet if you watch us, we all seek it out persistently and with great effort."

Because Singer thought that dissatisfaction was so fundamental to all of our lives, he tried to make it one of his ideals. It appears in a fantastic number of images, e.g., for Singer, in the images of tragedy and comedy in the arts, in music as well as in drama. He had the image of the enternal mountain-climber, who, incidentally, must often go down in order to climb higher. It is an Everest without a top to it. I want to make one adjustment to Singer's ideal-seeking philosophy: not only should we be engaged in seeking ideals, but we should also conscientiously be engaged in trying to find out what they should be. It is not unexpected that the question of what ideals we as human beings should be seeking is like any other question, theoretical or factual, namely, that it must keep changing. What the Utopians of the nineteenth century thought was an ideal community, we would no longer regard as ideal. That does not mean that they were wrong to try to design utopias. They were right to have experimented. The same remark applies to Marx. Whatever it is we find as ideals in Marx have to be adjusted in today's society and will have to be adjusted in time to come.

Put into Jungian terms, every proposed ideal has a negative-shadow side to it, something that is not good. It may require, for example, as in Plato, that there be a group of elite to run things, or, as in any other ideal, discomfort for many who have to live in the ideal city or ideal university. Both Russ and I have been engaged in designing ideal universities. Any one of you could well criticize the ideals we have proposed.

That remark takes me back to Singer's first question: What is the distance between A and B on the surface of the earth at a given moment of time? The meaning of that question depends not only on the measurement instruments and calibration, but also on what the metric distance means and what the metric time means. We are right now in a revolution in physics in which the question of what the metric time means is crucial in changing our minds about time. Just as we had to do it in Einstein's time, we are redoing it today.

I had not planned that this final chapter would come to a conclusion except that I would stop writing. I hope that this will be the first of many chapters in the sense that it is not the last. So much more needs to be said about the practical philosophy that Singer inspired in all of us, as well as about the philosophies that inspired him.

137

INDEX